Getting a Grip On The Basics
For Teens

a bible study for teens

13-19 years

By
Beth Jones

VALLEY PRESS
PUBLISHERS

3rd Printing

Getting A Grip On The Basics For Teens
Building A Firm Foundation For The Victorious Christian Life
ISBN   0-9717156-8-8
ISBN   978-0-9717156-8-4

Copyright 2003 Beth Ann Jones

Published By Valley Press Publishers
995 Romence Road
Portage, Michigan 49024

Contents

Dedication

This Book Is Dedicated To...

My four children - Meghan, Annie, Luke and Eric...

Meghan - you have a tender heart and you've been a great example to Annie, Luke & Eric.

Annie - you are the sunshine of our family, I love your spunk and charm.

Luke - you have a sweet heart for the Lord and I love your honesty.

Eric - you have a sensitive heart, you're truly a leader and you make me laugh.

All the teens at Kalamazoo Valley Family Church...

it's fun to watch you grow into beautiful young people who really love God,

who are not ashamed to worship Jesus,

and who have a heart for reaching out to other teens with His good news.

My nieces and nephews...

Hannah, Tiffany, Matthew, Erica, Chelsea, Morgan, Billy, Taylor, Sam, and Charlie,

it's fun to "watch and pray" for you as you grow up into

gorgeous, smart, sweet and talented young people who love God!

Special Thanks To...

Jeff Jones...

my husband, who demonstrates God's love to me every day

and who encourages me to keep writing!

Juli DeGraaf...

for her happy smile and cheerful voice,

not to mention her fine editing skills and daily assistance!

Craig and Andrea Seawell...

our Youth Directors, for their expertise and very helpful input.

Jennifer Parsons...

for her proofing skills and help.

Praying Friends...

the wonderful group of dear heartfelt friends and pray-ers

who pray for me and books like this.

A Note To Parents & Student Ministry Leaders

We are excited about helping teens get a grip on the basics of God's Word! Today's young people are facing many challenges, temptations and world influences. It's a different world for our teenagers than it was when we were teens! The youth culture is rapidly changing. Young people don't talk on the phone like we used to do after school, they instant message, email and chat with "their people" online. They have their own lingo and abbreviations for everything. Between the internet, tv, videos, movies, video games, music, the occult, fashion, advertising in magazines, the decor of many in-mall stores, the school bus, the lunch room and neighborhood...and even in some youth groups our kids are potentially being exposed to more lust, temptation, sin, pornography, susbtance abuse, wise-in-their-own-eyes rebellious attitudes, apathetic paradigms and unwanted pregnancies than when many of us were teens.

Thank God for young people who are willing to stand up and step out to be a bold, cool, loving Christian kid that others look up to! We believe God is raising up thousands of young people who really know Jesus, that know His Word and that are filled with His Spirit. They will be unashamed and unapologetic in their walk with God and their stance in God's Word, and they will take ground from the enemy by witnessing to their friends and family with boldness!

That is the heart behind *Getting A Grip On The Basics For Teens*. It's our goal to help young people know God by learning how to study their own Bibles, looking up their own verses and discovering the revelation truths of God's Word for themselves! It's exciting to know that teens can learn and obtain the revelation knowledge of the Word and come into a real relationship with God, where they taste and see that the Lord is good!

We can see from Bible history, as well as from current events, that the enemy doesn't wait until kids are in college to begin to lure them into a life of ungodliness and evil. The devil is working overtime to snatch children as soon as possible and he is using every form of literature, media, entertainment and business enterprise to do it! As parents and youth leaders, we need a more proactive approach to training our children in true Christianity. The youth culture is rapidly changing, and we need to equip our kids with the Word for the things this generation faces every day. That's one of the reasons we have written this book - we want to arm parents, church leaders and youth workers with a tool they can use to truly help kids get a grip on the basics of God's Word. We want to help Christian kids become so comfortable in their knowledge of God that they can be bold and strong when faced with peer pressures and temptations.

That is our goal in this workbook! We want to plant the seeds of God's Word into the hearts of teens so they develop strong roots and grow up to be strong, successful and prosperous in all they do!

What can you do as a parent or youth ministry leader while your child studies *Getting A Grip On The Basics For Teens*?

Here Are Some Ideas For Parents And Youth Ministry Workers

1. *Study with them! Make it a team event! Teach a "Get A Grip" class! We've given lots of "surplus" information in this book, so feel free to help your teen keep a pace that is best for him or her.*

2. *Pray for your teen. I highly encourage you to pray the prayers found in Ephesians 1:14-20 and Colossians 1:9-12 for your child each day!*

3. *I encourage your teens to use the New Living Translation or the New International Version or perhaps the New King James Version of the Bible for this workbook, so that they can understand the Scriptures in a language at their level.*

4. *Ask your child what they are learning and how God is speaking to their hearts as they study His Word, and help them to "do the Word" each week.*

A Note To Teens

You are about to begin an awesome journey in God's Word. Did you know that Jesus loves you, for real? The Bible is full of stories of God's love for young people! Did you know God is looking for Christian teens who will stand up and be counted? God is looking for Christian kids who are so comfortable in their knowledge of God that they can be bold and strong when faced with peer pressures and temptations. God wants Christian kids to know who they are in Christ, to have a prayer life, to know the Word and to live by faith! God is looking for you! God has always looked for young people He could use and there are many kids in the Bible that did mighty things for God!

Here Are Some Guidelines For You As You Study "Getting A Grip On The Basics For Teens"

1. *First, I want you to know that you can be an on-fire, cool, smart, happening teenager who loves God with all your heart! You can be an example of what it's like to be a real Christian to your friends!*

2. *If you have never studied the Bible before, let me give you a quick overview.*

   • *There are two major parts to the Bible - The Old Testament and the New Testament.*
   • *There are 66 Books in the Bible.*
   • *We will look up "references" in the Bible, which means we will look up the book name, the chapter number and the verse number. For example: Genesis 1:1 or Matthew 28:19. These are Bible references.*

3. *Pray and ask God to help you understand His Word and get to know Him better.*

4. *Set aside some time each week to do your lesson. Maybe you could use part of your Sunday afternoon to spend time with God in your Bible. Take your time to study each chapter in the workbook...this isn't a race! Look up each verse in your own Bible and read the verses thoroughly. Find a highlighter so that you can underline the verses in your Bible.*

5. *Be sure to double-check your Bible references. For example, notice that there is a difference between "John" and "1 John".*

6. *Once you have looked up the verse, fill in the blanks in your workbook.*

7. *Expect God to teach you more about Himself and how much He loves you!*

A. The Big Question

Do you know for sure where you will go when you die? How do you know if you are a Christian? What must you do to be "saved" and on your way to heaven? Does going to church or being a good person make you a Christian? Are you a Christian just because your parents are Christians? Does it really matter what you believe? Have you ever thought about where you will spend eternity? Where will you go after you die? God has told us how to know for sure where we will go after we die. He has given us the map to Him and to heaven in His book, the Bible. Let's look at it.

B. The Road Map To Get To Heaven

1. John 3:16-21

    This is the famous Scripture "3:16" that you always see on TV at national football games, in graffiti under a bridge, or on someone's t-shirt. What is this verse telling us?

    What is God's heart toward the world?_____

    What did He give us?_____

    If we believe in Jesus, what does God give us?_____

    To whom does God give eternal life?_____

    Did Jesus come to condemn the world?_____

    What did He come to do for the world?_____

    Why is it that people won't come to Jesus, the Light?_____

    _____

2.   1 John 5:11-13

Who gives us eternal life?_____

Where is this life?_____

Who has eternal life?_____

Who doesn't have eternal life?_____

What do you have if you believe in Jesus and have Him as your Lord?_____

In your own words, what is eternal life?_____

C.   Do You Know You Have Eternal Life?

Based upon the two passages we have studied, do you know for sure where you will go when you die?

__ Yes, I know for sure that I have eternal life and I am going to heaven.

How do you know?_____

__ No, I am not sure if I have eternal life and I don't know if I will go to heaven.

If you are not sure you have eternal life, or if you have questions you would like answered, then our study in the Bible will help you to know for sure if you have eternal life.

MY STORY: *I remember when I was a really little kid; I wondered where I would go when I died. My sisters and I would talk about it. I didn't know how to be sure I was going to heaven. We would try to figure out how long eternity was and we could never get to the end of forever. We wondered, what happens to people after they die? Everytime a famous person died, we wondered, "Where did they go?" When I was a teenager, I would lie in bed at night and think about eternity and where I would end up. I didn't know where I was going to go when I died and it scared me and made me feel unsettled. Finally, when I was 19 years old, I found out that Jesus said He was "the way, the truth and the life" and no one could go to the Father except through Him, and I realized that He was the way to heaven. I debated about becoming a Christian for a while, because I thought if you became a*

Christian that your life would become boring. God patiently worked on my heart and finally, when I was 19 years old I asked Jesus to be the Lord of my life and to come into my heart to forgive my sins. He did! I knew that I was a Christian and that I would go to heaven when I died. It was a happy day for my heart! I also found out that being a Christian is the most adventure-filled life on planet earth!

D.   Who Is Jesus?

Jesus is the most important person in history! He is more important than any president or king or any sports hero or movie star. Jesus is in a different league than any other religious leader in history. For example, many religious leaders like Confucius, Buddha, Mohammed and others have made claims to be prophets or teachers of God, but do they have the credentials to be who they claimed to be? Jesus Christ claimed to be God, in the flesh. Does He have the credentials to be believed? This is a critical issue. In today's society, everyone is trying so hard to be "politically correct" and "tolerant" and "non-offensive" to others. While it is generally a good rule to get along with people and be accepting of others and their beliefs, at some point as a Christian you need to know Who you believe, why you believe and then have the courage and just plain old guts to stand up for what you believe in. As a Christian, you need to be "unashamed of the gospel of Jesus Christ" even if it means that you potentially offend some people, or you are rejected or shunned because of your faith in the One who claimed and proved Himself to be God.

Jesus is different from any other religious leader. Here's why. Jesus didn't claim to be just a religious teacher, prophet or teacher – He claimed to be God! Jesus proved that He is God! Have you ever thought about that? God became a Man and walked on the planet He created!

MY STORY: *I am the oldest of four sisters. When we were little and then when we were teens, we would talk about Jesus. One day we kept talking about how amazing it was that Jesus was God and that God came to his own planet. How humbling for Jesus to become a baby and then walk on the planet He made. That thought boggled our minds! God walked on the earth He made - isn't that amazing? The sad thing is that the people He made rejected Him when He came to His own planet; and what is even sadder is that today people still reject Him.*

1.   Luke 1:68-70

         What does this verse tell us that God sent us?_____

2.   John 4:24-26

What is God looking for?_____

What is Jesus called?_____

3.   Colossians 1:15-17

Who is Jesus the visible image of?_____

How long has Jesus existed?_____

4.   John 10:11

What did Jesus call Himself?_____

What does He do for people?_____

5.   John 14:6

What did Jesus say about Himself?_____

_____

E.   Why Do We Need Jesus?

We need Jesus because we have sinned. Jesus is the only One who can forgive us of our sins. He's the only One who paid the high price for our sins. Think of it this way.

TAKING A TEST: Think about taking a test at school. What if your teacher told you that the only people that could pass the test were those who got 100%? Only the students who got every question correct could pass the test. If you took the test and missed one question, you would not pass. If you took the test and missed all the questions, you would not pass. How many people do you know who would flunk the test? What if this happened...what if your teacher said that if just one person in the class got 100% on the test, she would give everyone in the class 100%? That would be a pretty good deal, wouldn't it? If one student got all the answers correct, you would get an A!

Guess what? That's why we need Jesus! All of us have flunked God's test. We have sinned. We have not been perfect. Do you know anyone who has never sinned? No, every person has sinned and is categorized by God as a "sinner". We needed someone else to get 100% on the test. Jesus came to the earth and lived a sinless life - He got 100% on God's test! At 33 years of age He laid down His life as our substitute and He layed down His life on the cross and then went to hell for three days as our substitute - we should have gone to hell because we flunked the test - but He went there for us! The good news of the gospel is simply this: if we believe and receive Jesus as our Lord, then God will credit our account with Jesus 100%. He will forgive all our sins and give us an A+ in His sight! It doesn't get any better than that!

Do you see how exciting this is? We need Jesus, and thank God He wants to help us! Let's look at this.

1.   How Does God Define Sin?

Are you a sinner? Maybe you've been taught that breaking the Ten Commandments is a sin. It is. Perhaps you know someone who is a real "sinner"... they're mean, they lie, they're disrespectful to their parents, teachers, policemen and anyone in authority, they swear, drink, smoke, get high and maybe deal drugs, they skip school and they sleep around. They are major sinners and they are breaking the Ten Commandments all the time.

But, get this - did you know that someone who is seen as a nice person can also be a "sinner"? It's true. You can be on the honor role, morally pure and wholesome, nice, obedient to your parents and authorities, and yet by breaking just one commandment you fall into the "sinner" category! The Bible says that if you keep nine commandments and just break one of the commandments, in God's eyes it's as if you have broken all Ten Commandments. (James 2:10-11) So, whether you're a hard core sinner breaking all of the commandments or a nice sinner who's only broken one commandment - you still have to deal with the reality that there is a sin problem.

Why is this? Sin is a heart issue and God is primarily concerned with our hearts. God is more concerned with the "sin nature" inside of each of us than He is with the various "sins" we commit. That sin nature, whether it causes us to commit one sin or one million sins, is what keeps us separated from God. Did you know that both "outwardly good" and "outwardly bad" people can have hearts full of pride, selfishness, greed, materialism, jealousy, envy, rage, hate, rebellion and even

5

religion? Jesus brought this to the attention of some of the "good" people of His day when He told them that they were beautiful on the outside, but inside they were full of dead men's bones! (Matthew 23:27-28) Some people were really religious, they went to church regularly, knelt, bowed, followed all the traditions of their religion and Jesus got on their case! He told them that they loved their religious traditions more than they loved God and His Word. (Matthew 15:3-9)

So, the question you want to ask yourself is this: What kind of things are going on *inside* your heart? What's coming *out* of your heart? Our hearts are filled with all kinds of things that are not acceptable to God when we are not Christians, but when Jesus becomes the Lord of our hearts, He forgives all our sins and makes us acceptable to God. Let's look at the heart issues of sin.

a. Mark 7:15-23

What did Jesus say would "defile" us, or mess us up? (verse 15)_____

Jesus was describing our "thought life" in verse 20 – what things make us unacceptable to God?

_____

b. Romans 14:23

God wants us to do everything we do by faith. He wants us to eat by faith. Drink by faith. Sleep by faith. Walk by faith. Live by faith. Anytime we doubt we should do something, that's a sign that we should not do it. According to this verse, if you do anything you believe is not right, what are you doing?

_____

c. James 4:17

When your heart or conscience tells you to do the right thing and you disobey your heart or conscience, what does God call this?_____

Think about a time you were tempted to do something that you knew was wrong. How did you handle it? How did your heart feel when you were tempted to swear, be mean to others, or do something that you knew was wrong and you did it anyway? Did you feel something "scratchy" on the inside? That was your heart or conscience trying to tell you to do the right thing. It is always a good idea to obey and follow your conscience. When our hearts know the right thing to do, we need to obey our hearts. When we are thinking of doing something, but then inside we have some doubts about whether we should do it or not, that is a good sign that we should not do it, because it will be sin for us. Does this make sense?

LYING: Think about a time you were tempted to lie. Let's say your parents asked you a question. You knew that if you told the truth you would get in trouble, so you were being tempted to tell a lie. Has that ever happened to you? What was going on inside your heart? What was going on inside your mind? You were the only one who knew the truth and your conscience was trying to tell you to be honest. Here's a piece of advice: it's always better to tell the truth and follow honesty! Your heart will feel right, even if you get in trouble! When I was in about 9th grade, I knew one person who was a world class liar! She could take any situation and create the most believable lie. She even lied when she didn't have to lie. The only problem was that eventually it caught up to her because she had to remember who she told which lie to. It got confusing and eventually she got busted and lost her credibility. People began to realize that she was just a liar and you couldn't trust anything she said. You don't want that reputation, do you?

MY STORY: *When I was growing up, my mom always said, "Honesty is the best policy." She hated lying! I remember at times I told the truth even when I knew it meant that I would get in trouble because I would get in even more trouble for lying. Somehow, it was instilled in me that lying was not a good thing. I wanted my heart to be clear and not feel guilty. I was terrible at lying! Anytime I told a lie, my heart felt so guilty that I would usually have to confess the truth to my parents so that my heart could feel clean again. Has that ever happened to you?*

Ok, let's look at an "official" Bible definition for sin and then let's talk about what happens when we sin and how God has sent Jesus to remedy the sin problem.

SIN: To sin means, "to miss the mark". Have you ever shot a bow and arrow? To sin means to miss the "bull's eye" of God's perfect target. When an arrow hits any of the rings outside the bull's eye, it has missed the mark. In the same way, our sin has caused us to miss the mark of God's perfection. Did you know there is a difference between our "sin nature" and our "sinful acts"? Sinful acts are the result of our sin nature. For example, have you ever seen dandelions growing in your yard? Those pretty yellow flowers are nothing more than weeds! If you wanted to get rid of the dandelions, what would you have to do? What if you mowed the lawn, would that get rid of the dandelions? Not really. They would only be gone for a day because the dandelion root is still in the ground: dandelions will be springing up all over the yard once again! The only way to totally get rid of the dandelions is to remove them from their very roots. Think of the dandelions as our "sins" and think of their roots as the "sin nature". God's biggest concern is with our sin nature. God knows that when he changes the root, our "sin nature", that our "sins" will also change.

2.   What Happens When We Sin?

   a.   Isaiah 59:2

           What is the result of sin?_____

   b.   Romans 6:23

           What is the "paycheck" we get for our sins?_____

           What free gift does God give us when we believe in Jesus?_____

DEATH: Death is not a pleasant topic to discuss. For many people, talking about death is a sad and scary subject. Many people are afraid to die. Have you ever thought about where you will go when you die? The Bible says that most of humanity, before they meet Jesus, is in bondage to the "fear of death". (Hebrews 2:15) Even though some people act like they are not afraid to die, or some people try to act cool and boast about how they will *"party with all their friends in hell"*, the reality is that in the deepest part of the heart of every person who does not know Jesus, there is a real fear of death and beyond. The good thing is that Jesus came to take away the sadness and scariness of death.

The Bible describes three types of death: *spiritual death, physical death* and *eternal death*. These are big topics, so we will just introduce them to you now. Physical death is what happens when a person stops breathing and their heart or brain stops functioning. Physical death is when a person's body dies. Spiritual death is when a person is separated from God. If a person is not born again and doesn't know Jesus as his/her personal Lord, then that person is spiritually dead. Again, to be spiritually dead means that a person is separated from God. Eternal death is the final condition of all those who don't know Jesus as their Lord. They will be separated from God for eternity.

3.   Is Everyone A Sinner?

Romans 3:22-26

We are made right in God's sight when we do what?_____

How many of us have sinned? (verse 23) _____

God declared that we are not guilty because Jesus did what for us?_____

F.   Jesus Had To Die For People Like Us

Jesus died for people just like you and me. We might look like nice people, and we may even go to church, but apart from Jesus we really are empty and sinful. Jesus came to solve the sin problem once and for all in order to give us a new forgiven heart; but He had to give His life in order to do that. Jesus died upon a cross and gave His life so that we could have eternal life. God had to "redeem" us legally from the penalty of sin.

Romans 5:6-11

How did God show us His great love?_____

Since we have been made right in God's sight, what are we saved from?_____

How does this make you feel in your heart?_____

9

BUMBLE BEES: Have you ever been stung by a bee? It hurts! Did you know that after a bumble bee stings you, it dies? The only consolation for being stung is knowing that the bee that stung you is going to die! Did you know that some people are allergic to bee stings? If they get stung, it can kill them. Imagine you were allergic to bumble bee stings and one day you and your dad are driving in your car when suddenly a bumble bee flies in the car! How would you feel? A little scared, right? You'd have your eye on the bee and you might be screaming for someone to kill the bee immediately! What if your dad saw the bumble bee and he put his arm out so that the bumble bee would land on him and sting his arm, instead of yours? That would sure be a loving dad, wouldn't it? If the bumble bee stung your dad, it would hurt him, but it would also take the stinger out of the bee and the bee would die! Then, you'd be safe! Did you know that Your Heavenly Father loves you and He did just that? We were allergic to the sting of sin and it would cause us to die and be separated from our Heavenly Father. God sent Jesus to Earth to take the sting of sin and death for us. When Jesus died on the cross for us, it was like He was stung by the "bee of sin" and He took all the pain for us. When He did this, He also took the "sting of death" away and now everyone who believes in and receives Jesus will never die, but they will spend eternity in Heaven with Him!

G.   Jesus Rose From The Dead

Do you know what separates Christianity from every other religion? The resurrection! What do we celebrate on Easter? Jesus Christ is Risen! He's not in the tomb. The tomb is empty because Jesus is alive! This is the crux of Christianity - if Jesus is not risen, our faith is in vain and we are believing a fairytale.

a.   1 Corinthians 15:3

Jesus died for our sins and He was buried. What happened on the third day?_____

How many people saw Jesus after He was risen from the dead?_____

b.   Matthew 28:1-10

What happened after they put Jesus in the tomb?_____

Describe this story in your own words:_____

_____

10

MY STORY: *Are you a musical person? Do you like to sing or whistle or hum? As a kid I always liked to sing, although not in public! When I was in third grade, I really didn't know Jesus personally, but in my heart I wanted to know God. It's interesting that God filled my heart with a song about Jesus being risen from the dead. I was looking outside at the sunny, blue-sky day and I started to sing this song:*

The hills are sunny, the flowers are in bloom,
The bees buzz around us, the birds fly by.
The air is clean and the grass grows green,
The children are playing in the sun.
They are rejoicing for Jesus has risen,
They are happy for what He did.
He has picked this day to wash our sins away,
Jesus Christ has risen.

Has God ever put a song in your heart? I'll bet He has. Sometime you ought to just sing from your heart and see what type of words come out! You might be suprised to find God giving you a song! If you remember the words, write them down. God is blessing you with words from heaven! It's an amazing thing that often times God is talking to young children and teenagers even before they really know Him. When I look back to third grade, when I was around 8 or 9 years old, God was filling my heart with songs from heaven and after I became a Christian at 19 years of age, the Lord continued to give me songs. So, no matter what age you are, start listening to and singing from your heart and see what type of songs the Lord gives you!

H. Jesus Is The Only Way To God

Jesus is God's only Savior. There is no one that can replace Him. He is the most important person in all of creation. This is so important to understand, because in today's culture many people want Jesus to be "one of many" ways to God. It's not politically correct in some places to believe in Jesus as the only way to God. In fact, some people will call you "intolerant" or "narrow-minded", a "bigot" and plenty of other names. As a true-blue Christian, you'll want to have your own heart conviction of who Jesus is. This might cost you some friendships. You might be rejected by some people. That's ok, you don't want to be some "wimpy, fair-weather, jelly-fish" Christian do you? You want to be a person who is not ashamed to call Jesus the Lord and more personally, your Lord! Let's look at this.

1.	Matthew 7:13-14

	How did Jesus describe the entrance to God's kingdom?_____

	How did Jesus describe the highway to hell?_____

2.	John 14:6

	Jesus said He was the_____, the _____ and the _____.

	Who can go to the Heavenly Father without Jesus?_____

3.	Acts 4:12

	Is there any other name, besides Jesus, that people can call on to be saved?_____

4.	1 Timothy 2:5

	How many mediators are there between God and man?_____

	Who is the Mediator?_____

5.	Ephesians 2:1-10

	This passage summarizes everything we have discussed in this section and describes the reason we need Jesus.

	What was the result of our sin?_____

	What did God do for us?_____

	Can we take any credit for being saved?_____

	What does God call "salvation"?_____

	What does God call us?_____

	Can you see that God has a plan for your life now that you are a Christian?_____

I.   Jesus Will Give Us A New Life

1.   2 Corinthians 5:17

When we believe in Jesus and receive Him into our lives, we become Christians.

What happens to us when we become Christians?_____

What type of life has begun?_____

2.   John 3:1-7

Jesus told Nicodemus that a person cannot see the kingdom of God unless he is what?

_____

BORN AGAIN: Being born again is also called the "new birth". When you are born again, you don't go back into your mother's womb to be born again, but your heart is born again! God gives you a brand new heart (or spirit) and now from your heart you can be friends with God. God welcomes you into a new Father/child relationship with Him. You are actually adopted into the family of God. You become a child of God and a member of His family when you accept Jesus as your Lord and are born again. Can you imagine that? You become a member of God's very own family! You become His son or daughter!

Maybe you have a very loving mom and dad or step-parents and a wonderful family, and when you become a born-again Christian you'll get to be in God's family, too! Maybe you don't have a very happy family and you only dream of what it would be like to live in a home where people love each other and where there is peace and happiness. Maybe your parents are divorced and you are being raised by a single parent in a difficult family situation. It's possible your home life makes you feel sad and depressed sometimes. Maybe you can't wait until you are old enough to move out of your home and create your own world and someday your own family. Well, you don't have to wait. You don't have to be sad and depressed, because when you become a born-again Christian you become a member of God's loving, healthy family. He really cares about you and He'll help you even if your home life is difficult!

MY STORY: *My parents were separated when I was 10 years old. They were divorced when I was 13. It was a very sad and scary and difficult time in my life. I was the oldest of four sisters and when my parents divorced, I felt responsible for my sisters. I also felt responsible for helping my mom get through the pain she was going through. I had to grow up in a quick hurry! Divorce is a mess. Even though my parents did their best to shield my sisters and me from all the details and pain they were experiencing, our world was still rocked by the divorce. I remember watching Pepsi commercials back then and seeing all those happy families. I wondered what it would be like to have a family like that. When I was in high school, I often wished that my dad lived with us so that I could cry on his shoulder when I was feeling rejected or feeling ugly, or feeling all the things that hormonal teenage girls feel! I didn't find out about Jesus and being a part of God's family until I was 19 years old. What a nice suprise to find out that I could be born-again into God's family and He wanted to be my 24/7 Father! His shoulder was always available!*

3.   John 1:12-13

Who gets to become a child of God?_____

You get to choose to believe on and receive Jesus as your Lord, and at that moment God adopts you into His family! You become His child forever.

J. How Do I Receive Jesus?

You can receive Jesus into your life by simply inviting Him to come into your heart. Have you ever heard your friends knock on the door of your house? When you heard the knock, what did you do? You opened the door and invited them inside, right? It's the same way with Jesus. He is knocking on the door of your heart and He wants you to answer His knock and invite Him into your life. It's really simple.

Here's the deal: Jesus is knocking on the door of your heart, but there is only one door handle and it's on your side of the door! Jesus won't barge into your life uninvited. He is a gentleman. He will wait for you to fully unlock the door and throw it open to invite Him into every part of your life. When you believe and say, "Jesus, I believe in You and I welcome You into my life to be the Lord of my life. You are free to move into every area of my life!" He will take you at your word and He'll move right in!

When you receive Jesus as your Lord, you become a "Christian"! To be a Christian simply means to be a follower of Christ. Acts 11:26 tells us about the first believers in the New Testament, who were called Christians.

When you become a Christian you are "saved." To be saved means quite a lot! The definition of being "saved" includes freedom from the penalty of sin, preservation, safety, welfare, healing, wholeness and complete and final deliverance from sin. We are saved to enjoy this life with God and after this life we are saved from hell! This is good news!

1.   Revelation 3:20

        What is Jesus doing?_____

        What does He want us to do?_____

        If we open the door to Jesus, what will He do?_____

2.   John 3:16

        Who can believe in Jesus?_____

        What are the results of believing?_____

3.   Romans 10:8-10

        Salvation comes from trusting whom?_____

        What are you supposed to confess with your mouth?_____

        What are you supposed to believe in your heart?_____

        What are the results?_____

        Did you know that God wants you to believe in Jesus from your heart, and He also wants you to say that Jesus is your Lord with your mouth?

CONFESS: To confess means to agree with God or to say that same thing about Jesus that God says. To confess our belief in Jesus means to agree and to say that Jesus is Lord. Confessing Jesus as Lord means that you are saying He is your Lord.

4.   Matthew 10:32,33

What does Jesus promise if you publicly acknowledge Him?_____

MY STORY: *I was raised as a Roman Catholic. I remember that I liked going to church as a kid because it made me feel close to God. I loved going to the Catholic church. I loved the smell of the incense. I learned to have a real awe and respect for God. I was taught about God the Father, Jesus and the Holy Spirit. However, when I was 10 years old, my parents were separated and eventually divorced and we stopped going to the Catholic church as a family. Sometimes I would walk to church by myself. It was about a 5 mile walk. There was something in my heart that wanted to know God, so when all my friends were skipping church and sitting in the K-Mart Red Grill, I was walking to church! It's funny to look back and realize that the God-shaped vacuum inside of me was truly "sucking" me toward God. When I was in junior high school, in 7th grade, God started to take a back seat in my life and I began to get real involved in sports and I began to experiment with all kinds of forbidden things.*

The first thing I began to do was to steal my mom's cigarrettes - Marlboro Reds. My friends and I would scavenge cigarettes from our parents and then smoke them in the mall bathrooms or behind the school. We were little hoodlums! The other thing I discovered in 7th grade was drinking. We started to drink Boone's Farm wine and Old Milwaukee beer at parties. Smoking cigarettes and drinking wine and beer was the beginning of a party life. From 7th grade until I was 19 years old my life revolved around playing sports and partying. Our group of 12 girls and 12 guys at school wanted to be cool, so we were the jocks and the partyers. Friday nights were made for partying. We started drinking at lunch. We'd sit in the McDonalds' parking lot and drink beer and smoke a few joints and then go back to school. After school we'd go to basketball practice or softball practice or whatever sport was in season and then we'd just start the party all over during the Friday night football or basketball game. By the 4th quarter we were usually wasted, and taking the party to the bonfire in the woods or to the hidden gravel pit or we were searching for the nearest keg. We pretty much lived to party.

The most amazing thing is that as far as the teachers and most parents were concerned, we were the "good kids"! We were not trouble makers. We were volunteers. We got good grades. We served on student council. We played sports. Many of us attended the local Catholic church and confession on occassion. Little did our parents know how much we partied!

During our senior year in high school two major events took place. During spring break our gang of friends - boys and girls - drove to Daytona Beach, Florida for a week of sun, fun and partying. Unfortunately, during that week 4 of our friends were killed in a tragic car accident. Their deaths made all of us think about life, death, heaven and hell. It was a sad and sober time.

At that same time two of my friends, Andrea and Linda, had a dramatic experience with God and they became "Christians"...we called them Jesus freaks! Their lives took a sudden turn as they quit partying and began toting their Bibles everywhere. We couldn't believe the change in them. We actually made fun of them, while at the same time we noticed that they carried a peace and happiness that the rest of us didn't have.

God has a sense of humor, because after I graduated from high school and entered college, Andrea ended up being my roommate at Western Michigan University! Andrea was on fire for the Lord and this was irritating to me because I was not done living my party life! I had known Andrea since 3rd grade and now here she is "Miss Religious"...reading her Bible and going to Bible Studies. I was reading trash novels and going to keggers! During my freshman year in college, Andrea talked to me about the Lord many times and I acted like I was quite disinterested. However, I remember that she shared three Bible verses with me that I couldn't get away from.

First, she shared the verse in Matthew 7:13-14, "You can enter God's Kingdom only through the narrow gate. The highway to hell is broad, and its gate is wide for the many who choose the easy way. But the gateway to life is small, and the road is narrow, and only a few ever find it." (NLT)

I realized in my heart that I was on the wide path going to hell. I wasn't a bad person, but I knew that I wasn't into God like Andrea was and I really didn't want God invading my life at the time. I walked around campus thinking, "I am doomed...I am on the wide path going to hell." However, I didn't run to God. I decided that maybe I could appease God and avoid becoming a religious freak by doing some good deeds. So, I started picking up trash in the dorm, thinking that might impress God.

17

Soon, Andrea shared another verse of Scripture with me found in Revelation 3:15-17, "I know all the things you do, that you are neither hot nor cold. I wish you were one or the other! But since you are like lukewarm water, I will spit you out of my mouth!" (NLT) I realized that my good deeds had not impressed God at all, in fact, I could see that I was lukewarm and He was about to spit me out of His mouth. I didn't like this at all! This verse got my attention and I realized that although I wasn't ready to commit my life to God, maybe I needed to get more religious, so I signed up to attend a weekend religious retreat at my church.

On that retreat I did feel as though God was trying to open my eyes and heart to Him, but I still thought if I became a "Christian" and really gave my life to the Lord, I would have to live this boring life of Bible studies and "praise the Lord's". I didn't want to give up the control of my life - I enjoyed being on the throne of my life and that meant I could party and do what I wanted to do, so I just acted a little more religious with the hopes that I could fake someone out.

It wasn't long until Andrea shared another verse that hit me between the eyes. This passage is found in Matthew 7:21-23 "Not all people who sound religious are really godly. They may refer to me as 'Lord,' but they still won't enter the Kingdom of Heaven. The decisive issue is whether they obey my Father in heaven. On judgment day many will tell me, 'Lord, Lord, we prophesied in your name and cast out demons in your name and performed many miracles in your name.' But I will reply, 'I never knew you. Go away; the things you did were unauthorized.'" (NLT) My heart was pierced, how could God know what I was doing? It was like He saw me and knew me! His response to my "religious activity" was that He never knew me! Wow, that really made me think. I walked around the campus thinking about the fact that I really didn't know God and I was on the wide path going to hell. So, what was I going to do about it?

For the next 6 months I secretly read the Bible. I didn't want anyone to know. A friend of Andrea's had given me a Bible and when I studied for chemistry I tucked it inside my chemistry book so no one would know I was reading it. As I read the Bible, for the first time it seemed that my eyes were being opened to things I had never known. It was like God was sitting on my shoulder and revealing my life and His mercy to me. I read the Gospel of John, then Romans and then Hebrews. As I read, it became clear to me that I was a sinner and I needed a Savior to rescue me.

Up until this point in my life, I had considered myself to be a good person. I certainly never thought of myself as a "sinner", in fact I had considered myself a pretty good person. However, when I read the Bible, it was like God knew my thoughts and the deeds I had committed and I was clearly a sinner. For the first time in my life, I realized that I needed a Savior to forgive me of all my sins and give me a clean slate.

By the end of my freshman year in college I knew that the time had come for me to make a decision to accept Jesus Christ. I knew I needed a Savior, but I was still living a double life. I was reading my Bible and asking for God's help in my life, but at the same time I was partying, smoking and getting high on a regular basis. I was still in charge of my life. I had not surrendered to Jesus Christ. I had not invited Him into my life. I had not confessed Him as Lord of my life. I recognized that there was a big square hole in my life and I had tried to fill it with every round peg - all the partying, being popular, having friends, music, and stuff but the square hole only got bigger!

In May of 1978 at the end of my freshman year, I decided that the time had come for me to get off the fence and invite Jesus into my life and become a born-again Christian. One day I was visiting with one of my other high school friends, Michelle, who was also deciding whether she wanted to become a Christian (another long story!) and while sitting at her kitchen table I had a little wrestling match going on in my head. One part of me said, "today you need to decide so just tell Michelle you are going to be a Christian and be one!" The other part of my head said, "no, don't tell Michelle anything, just keep living your double party life." Finally, sitting right there in her kitchen I made my decision for Christ and decided to tell Michelle and I said, "Uh, well, um...I am going to be a Christian from now on." When I made that statement it was like Jesus said, "that's all I need" and He moved right in to my heart, forgave my sins and He's been there ever since!

Instantly I felt relieved inside and a great sense of peace settled in my heart. At last I had found the square peg for the square hole in my heart! It was the most amazing thing...the very next day I woke up with peace and internal joy. The sky was bluer. The birds were singing more sweetly. My eyes were opened! However, I was so new at all this "God stuff" I really didn't know quite what to do and I realized I needed some help in learning how to get to know God better. This workbook, "Getting A Grip On The Basics For Teens," is the result of my getting to know Jesus better over the past 25 years. The decision to invite Jesus into my life was the beginning of the most fun, "intoxicating" adventure I have ever known and I know it will be for you too!

So, where are you? Perhaps it's time for you to make a decision, too, and invite Jesus Christ to be the Lord of your life. Maybe you need to give up your "double life" of being a church goer or a nice person or a partyer on one hand and then pretending to be a Christian on the other hand. Take a few minutes to read "Real Christians Do It" and make your decision to invite Jesus Christ into your life today.

Now, if you were to die today, would you spend eternity with God? Would you like to make the decision to invite Jesus to be the Lord of your life? Would you like Jesus to forgive you of all your sins and give you a brand new heart? Answer these two questions before we pray.

1. Do you believe that Jesus is Lord? _____

2. Do you believe that God raised Jesus from the dead?_____

If you answered "yes" to these two questions, you are ready to invite Jesus to be the Lord of your life. When you ask Jesus into your life, you will be totally changed on the inside: in your heart. It's sort of like the caterpillar that is changed into a beautiful butterfly. God wants everyone to make this change. He wants you to become a beautiful Christian full of His life. If you have never asked Jesus into your heart before, would you like to do that now? This is the most important decision you will ever make in this life on Earth.

Asking Jesus into your heart means you can spend eternity, forever with Him now and in heaven. He wants to be your best friend and Lord, and help you with everything you do. He wants to be in the driver's seat, behind the steering wheel of your life. When you invite Him into your life, He will give you a new heart and wash away all your sins. He will become your closest friend. Are you ready to invite Jesus into your life? Let's pray this prayer together to invite Jesus to be your Lord and Savior.

"Dear God, I come to You and I know that I need You. I have sinned and I need Your forgiveness. Jesus, I believe that You died for me on the cross and I believe that God raised You from the dead. I believe that You are Lord Jesus, and I invite you into my heart to be the Lord of my life. I thank You for forgiving all my sins and giving me a brand new heart. I am now Your child. I am born again into Your family. I am saved and now I know I will spend forever in heaven with You when I die. Thank You, Heavenly Father. Thank You, Jesus. Amen."

Congratulations! This is the most important decision you have ever made! Jesus is now the Lord of your life! In the rest of this study, we will learn how to get to know Him better. If this is the first time you prayed a prayer to receive Jesus as your Lord, let's write it down!

Today, _____ (day/date), at _____(time)

I _____(name) prayed to receive Jesus as my Lord.

Signed:_____(your name)

Witness:_____(your parents/other)

A. How To Be Sure You Are A Christian

Are you sure you are a Christian? Have you ever had any doubts? If you've had doubts, you are normal! One of the enemy's first tricks is to try to make you doubt that you are a Christian. He will try to plant thoughts in your mind to make you <u>think</u> or <u>feel</u> as though you are not really a sincere Christian. One day you may really *think* you are a born-again Christian and the next day you may not, so you can see that your "thinking" is not a good judge to go by. The enemy may also try to make you feel as if you are not saved. One day you may really *feel* like a Christian. You may feel really happy or maybe you cried tears as you responded to an altar call one day, but the next day you may feel as if you are not saved and not in God's presence. So, your "feelings" are not a good judge to go by either. Do you get the idea?

1.   Have you ever had any doubts about being a Christian?_____

2.   What did you do to combat those doubts?_____

How do you know that you are truly a born-again Christian? How do you know that you will live forever with God in heaven when you die? How do you resist the enemy when he works against your mind and feelings? The first thing you need to know is that being a Christian or being saved is based on the fact of what God has said in His Word, not on your brain's thoughts or emotional feelings.

You must go by the facts, not feelings or thoughts! Facts do not change. What are the facts? God's Word contains the unchanging facts. God's Word, the Bible, is the only authority for your Christian life. God knows every fact; His Word contains the facts. We do not depend upon feelings or emotions to be Christians, born again or saved; we are Christians, born again and saved by placing our trust, or our faith, in God and His Word. Let's take a "test" to remind ourselves that we are truly Christians. We are born again. We are saved.

B.   Take The "I Know I Am A Christian" Test

1.   Facts

      Does the Bible or Bible facts ever change?_____

2.   Feelings

      Do our feelings ever change?_____

      What determines how we feel?_____

3.   Faith

      What happens if our faith or our trust is in our feelings?_____

      What happens if our faith or trust is in the fact of God's Word?_____

MY STORY: *One of the best stories I have ever heard to describe the difference between fact, faith and feelings is about a train. (I found this in the "Four Spiritual Laws" booklet, written by Bill Bright and published by Campus Crusade for Christ.) Imagine, or better yet draw, three train cars on a piece of paper. The engine car we call "Fact", the caboose we call "Feelings", and the middle car we call "Faith". The "Facts" - engine car - represent God's Word. The "Feelings" - caboose - represent our emotions and thoughts. The "Faith" - middle car - represents where we put our trust. In order for the train to run down the track, the engine must pull it, right? Don't you think it would be impossible to pull the train by the caboose? In the same way, our Christian life is pulled down the track of each day when we place our faith in the facts of God's Word. We don't pull our Christian life down the daily track with the caboose and place our faith in our emotions or mind. Some days our feelings will be up and some days our feelings will be down, some days we may think God is with us and some days we may doubt, so it is not a good idea to let the caboose of emotions or thoughts direct our lives! We need to just choose to put our faith in the facts of God's Word and our lives will stay on track!*

C.   What Are The Facts We Believe?

1.   1 John 5:11-13

How do you know that you have eternal life?_____

2.   John 1:12

How do you know you became a child of God?_____

3.   Colossians 1:14

What do you know you have received for your sins?_____

4.   2 Corinthians 5:17

What have you become as a Christian?_____

What has happened to the old you?_____

5.   Romans 8:16

Who speaks to our hearts to tell us that we are God's children?_____

6.   Hebrews 13:5

What do you know that Jesus Christ will never do?_____

Take time to journal your experience with God by completing the "Real Christians Do It" section.

Now it's time to just do it! Let's take action on what we've studied.

Are you sure that you are a Christian?_____

How do you know you are a Christian - on what authority do you base your certainty?

_____

What Scriptures do you believe that let you know that you indeed are a Christian?

_____

On the inside cover of your Bible (or somewhere you can keep a permanent record), write down the date and the time you received Jesus as your Lord. You may have to guess on the date and time if it was a long time ago. (You can ask your mom or dad if they remember the time you first invited Jesus to be your Lord.) Whenever the enemy tries to confuse you or discourage you with doubts about being a Christian, born again or saved, just tell him the date and time you invited Jesus Christ to be your Lord.

Once again, let's write down this important information! If you need a reminder, just look back at the end of Chapter 1.

The Date I Became A Christian By Asking Jesus Into My Heart:_____

The Location and Time:_____

Who Was With Me:_____

A. What Is God Like?

When you become a Christian you begin a personal relationship with God. He is a Person – not a force, or vapor, or power, or an invisible eye. He wants to talk to you, and He wants you to talk to Him. God loves you and He wants to be your very best friend. Think about your friends. Who is your best friend? When did you meet? How did you become best friends? When you meet new friends, it takes many hours of talking, playing and hanging out to really get to know them, doesn't it? God has become your friend, and He is the most interesting and loving person you will ever know. Now it's going to take time, the rest of your life, to get to know and enjoy your very own personal relationship with God - your Heavenly Father, Jesus your Lord, and the Holy Spirit your Helper.

Did you know the deep heart desire of every person is to know God? Every person has a built-in spiritual hunger that only God can satisfy. The primary ways to get to know God are spending time talking to Him in prayer (which we will look at in our next lesson), and spending time letting Him talk to you from His Word, the Bible (which we will look at in a future lesson.) In this lesson, let's take a few moments to see what your new friend is like. He has revealed Himself in the Bible. How do the following verses describe God?

1.   Who Is God?

Matthew 28:19

There is only one God, but He reveals Himself in three persons. That makes our brains go "tilt", doesn't it? Let's look at which three persons make up the Godhead (or Trinity).

God the_____

God the_____

God the _____

Get this. You can get to know God the Father personally. You can really get to know Him as your personal Heavenly Father. You can get to know Jesus as your Lord, as your Healer, as your good Shepherd, as your friend who sticks closer than a brother! You can get to know the Holy Spirit personally, too. The Holy Spirit lives in you! He's your Helper, your Comforter, your Counselor, your Strengthener, your Truth Guide and much more!

2.　What do these verses tell us about God as our Father?

　　a.　Matthew 7:11

　　God the Father is the giver of_____

　　b.　John 4:24

　　God is a_____

　　c.　James 1:17

　　Whatever is good and perfect comes from God above.

　　He never_____

3.　What do these verses tell us about Jesus our Lord?

　　a.　John 8:12

　　Jesus is_____

　　b.　John 10:14

　　Jesus is a good_____

　　c.　Hebrews 13:8

　　Jesus is the same_____, _____ and _____

4.   What do these verses tell us about the Holy Spirit?

   a.   1 Corinthians 3:16

          The Holy Spirit lives where?_____

   b.   John 14:26

          The Holy Spirit will _____ me all things

          The Holy Spirit will _____ me of all things Jesus has told me

   c.   John 16:13, 14

          The Holy Spirit _____ me into all the truth

          He _____ me things that will happen in the future

   d.   Romans 8:14

          The children of God are _____ by the Holy Spirit

   e.   Romans 8:16

          The Holy Spirit speaks to our hearts and tell us what?_____

I want to encourage you to use the verses you just looked up about God the Father, Jesus and the Holy Spirit and "pray" these verses back to God and let Him know you want to get to know Him like these verses describe. Take time to ponder these verses and let your heart grab on to them. You will find yourself knowing God more personally and more deeply. He won't just be stories in a book, but He will be a living, personal God to you!

B.   Who Are We?

God made us! We were created in the image and likeness of God. God is a three-part being – Father, Son and Holy Spirit - and He has made us to be a three-part person.

1 Thessalonians 5:23

What three things, that make up the three parts of a human being, does God want to be kept blameless?

_____, _____ and _____

Our <u>spirit</u> is also called the heart, the inner man or the hidden man of the heart. Our spirit is the real, deep down inside person we are! The person who lives behind your eyes, the real you, is a spirit. Your spirit or heart is the part of you that only you and God know! Our spirit is the part of us that really connects with God – it's the part of us that God talks to and lives in.

Our <u>soul</u> is our personality and includes our mind, our will and our emotions. Our soul is the part of us that thinks mental thoughts and expresses our emotions of joy or tears, and our will is the part of us that makes decisions to do things or to not do things. Our soul is the part of us that learns and studies and is filled with knowledge.

Our <u>body</u> is what you look at in the mirror! It's like the "house" our spirit and soul live in. Our body is our "earth suit". Our body is the part of us that has the five physical senses of sight, hearing, taste, touch and smell that help us live in the natural world.

God wants us to be led by our spirits, but have you noticed that sometimes your soul (mind, emotions and will) and your body fight your spirit? In other words, in your heart or spirit you know the right things to do, but your mind may try to convince you to do wrong things, or your feelings may not want to do the right thing, or your body may want to pull you in another direction. You have to choose with your will to allow your spirit to win!

APOLOGIZING: For example, have you ever been mean to someone, maybe to your brother or sister? Did your heart or spirit tell you that you should apologize to them? Did you feel like apologizing? Did you want to apologize? Now you have a choice to make. You can let your feelings dominate you, or you can let your spirit or heart dominate you. If you choose to let your spirit lead you, you will apologize and you will have peace in your heart. If you choose to let your soul or body win out, you will feel unrest in your heart and maybe even anger. It's always best to obey and follow your heart or spirit.

It's helpful to understand that we are a three-part person, isn't it? God wants us to grow strong in our spirits by knowing Him and His Word. He wants us to fill our souls with His

Word, too, so that our thoughts and emotions and will are balanced, healthy and at peace. He wants our bodies to be strong and healthy, too, so that he can bless our whole life.

C. How Do I Get To Know God Better?

You can get a head start in living a blessed, prosperous, fruitful, adventure-filled life with God if you will start seeking God as a young person. Proverbs 8:17 tells us this very thing: *"I love them that love me; and those that seek me early shall find me..."* God is telling us that He loves those that love Him, and those that seek Him and His wisdom early in life will find it! Here are some ways you can seek God early in your life.

1.   Be Like Enoch

        Did you know that Enoch was a friend of God? God liked Enoch a lot. The name Enoch means "dedicated". Enoch was dedicated to God. Let's look at his life.

        a.   Genesis 5:23-24

                How long did Enoch live?_____

                Can you imagine that?

                What type of relationship did he have with God?_____

                God loved Enoch so much that Enoch didn't even die! God just lifted Enoch off planet Earth and took him to heaven!

        b.   Hebrews 11:5

                What did God think about Enoch?_____

2.   Put God First In Your Life

        Matthew 6:33

        What does God want you to put first in your life?_____

        What will God do for you if you put Him and His kingdom first?_____

31

3. Love And Seek God With Your Whole Heart

Have you ever felt loved by your parents or family or friends? Did it make you feel good to know that someone loved you from their heart? Did you know that God likes it when we love Him with our whole heart? In fact, God's eyes are searching the whole earth to find people with hearts totally in love with Him. Will His eyes find you?

a. 2 Chronicles 16:9

What are God's eyes doing?_____

Who is He looking for?_____

What will He do for those who are fully committed to Him?_____

b. Psalm 119:2

Describe the people who seek after God with their whole heart._____

c. Jeremiah 29:11-13

What kind of plans does He have for you?_____

If you seek God earnestly, or with your whole heart, what will you find?_____

d. Hebrews 11:6

What does God do for those who sincerely seek Him?_____

e. Ecclesiastes 12:1

When should you seek God?_____

D. God Talks To & Uses Young People

Did you know that you are never too young to seek the Lord? To know the Lord? To be used of the Lord? God has a mighty plan for your life and if you will put Him first and spend time

32

getting to know Him, you can be just like the young kids of the Bible who knew God. No matter how old you are, you can know God deeply! God will cause you to be a leader among your friends if you will put Him first. Let's look at several examples of young people that sought God!

1.   Luke 2:41-52

How old was Jesus in this story?_____

What was Jesus discussing with the older religious teacher in verse 46?_____

What do you think Jesus meant in verse 49?_____

How did Jesus respond to his parents in verse 51?_____

How did Jesus grow according to verse 52?_____

2.   Luke 1:26-38

Mary was a single, engaged young girl when God chose her to be the mother of His Son! What an honor! What if Mary had been a rebellious, backslidden teenager? Mary was an obedient, sweet-spirited young lady.

What did the angel Gabriel say to Mary in verse 28?_____

What did Mary say in verse 38?_____

3.   1 Timothy 4:12

Is this verse talking about an old person or a young person?_____

Even though you are young, God is instructing you to be an example.

In what areas are you to be an example?

_____

4.   Genesis 37:1-7

God gave a young man a dream that described God's plan for his life.

How old was Joseph when God gave him a special dream?_____

5.   2 Kings 11:21; 12:2

How old was Jehoash when he became a king?_____

What did the Lord think of Jehoash?_____

6.   2 Kings 15:1-3

How old was Azariah when he became a king?_____

What did the Lord think of Azariah?_____

7.   2 Kings 21:1-2

How old was Manasseh when he became a king?_____

What did the Lord think of Manasseh?_____

8.   2 Kings 22:1-2

How old was Josiah when he became a king?_____

What did the Lord think of Josiah?_____

9.   2 Kings 24:8-9

How old was Jehoiachin when he became a king?_____

What did the Lord think of Jehoiachin?_____

10.   2 Chronicles 26:1-5

How old was Uzziah when he became a king?_____

What did the Lord think of Uzziah?_____

As long as Uzziah sought the Lord, what did God do for him?_____

Can you see that it's possible to know God and be used by Him as a teenager? Why not develop your strategy for getting to know God better in the "Real Christians Do It" section.

It's time to do it! What is your plan for getting to know God? Do you have one? Some people call it their "devotional time", some people call it their "quiet time". What would you like to call your time with the Lord?

Sure, on one hand you can talk to the Lord all day no matter where you are, but on the other hand, setting aside some uninterupted time to spend with the Lord in His Word and in prayer is the single most powerful way to get to know Him personally.

Why not make a decision to spend time reading the Bible each day? How about your prayer life? Do you have a regular time for talking to the Lord? Remember, it takes time to get to know someone as your best friend. So, schedule your time with the Lord right now.

I plan to read my Bible each day @ this time:_____ for this long:_____.

I plan to pray to the Lord each day @ this time:_____ for this long:_____.

<u>Other things you may want to do:</u>

• listen to and sing from your heart to God with a worship CD
• write your prayers in a letter to God
• write down the thoughts/revelations God gives you from His Word
• write down songs of thanks, praise or worship to the Lord that you make up from your own heart

Prayer is simply talking to God, from your heart. You can talk to God about anything and everything, just like you would talk to your parents or your best friend. Through praying to the Lord you will develop a really close relationship with Him.

Have you ever thought about it? When you pray, you have a meeting with the God of the Universe! You are talking to the King of kings and the Lord of lords! He is also your very own Heavenly Father. Wow! Isn't that wonderful?

The devil doesn't like prayer! He doesn't want you to get close to God. He will try to distract you from praying by keeping you too busy with other things. You need to make a decision to talk to your Heavenly Father often during the day, whether you're at home, at school or any other place. If you will do this, prayer will become as natural to you as breathing.

Let's look at how we can pray.

A.   Jesus Prayed

1.   Mark 1:35

When did Jesus pray?_____

Where did He go to pray?_____

2.   Luke 6:12

Where did Jesus go to pray?_____

How long did He pray?_____

Wow! That's a long time to pray, isn't it? Jesus loved God so much and wanted to spend time talking to Him. He needed to get alone so He could talk to His Father.

Do you have a special place you like to pray?_____

3.   Matthew 6:6

Where did Jesus tell us to pray?_____

You might not have a closet to pray in, but the idea is to find a quiet place that you can shut out the distractions and noise of the world around you so that you can be alone with your Heavenly Father. That might be in your bed under your covers! It could be in a special place in your home. It might be a tree fort. It could be the bathtub! Anywhere you can be alone with the Lord is a great place to pray and talk to God!

Who do we pray to?_____

What will God do in response to our prayers?_____

B.   Attitudes In Prayer

God wants you to pray from your heart; that is the most important thing. What is the main thing you learn from each of these verses?

1.   Psalm 5:1-3_____

2.   Psalm 62:8_____

3.   John 4:23-24

Did you know that "praise and worship" is a special kind of prayer? It's the kind of prayer that God is looking for. What does this verse tell us about this kind of prayer?

_____

C.   God Promises To Answer Your Prayer

1.   Matthew 7:7-11

What does God want us to do?_____

If we ask, seek and knock, what will God do?_____

What type of gifts will our Heavenly Father give to those who ask?_____

2.   1 John 5:14

If we ask for anything in line with God's will, is He listening?_____

If we know He is listening, what can we be sure of?_____

Did you know that God's Word tells us what God's will is? If you want to know if something is in line with God's will, look in the Bible to see what God has already told us about His will. The more you read God's Word, the more you will think like God thinks and you will know His will. While you are growing up spiritually, you should also ask your parents or pastor or more mature Christians to help you see God's will in His Word.

3.   John 15:7

God promises to answer our prayers, but before He will answer our requests, He tells us that we must do something. What are we to do?

_____

By reading God's Word on a regular basis, His Word and His will gets in your heart and you will stay connected to Him!

4.   John 16:23-24

Jesus tells us that once He was raised from the dead, we could go directly to the Father in His name and make our prayer requests. What did He promise?

_____

6.   Mark 11:24

What did Jesus say we could pray for or about?_____

What is the condition to receiving an answer to our prayers?_____

The role of faith or believing in prayer is very important. In fact, the Bible says it's impossible to receive anything from God without faith! (James 1:5-8)

Isn't it an amazing thing to think that the God of the universe is interested in answering your prayers? He is a loving, generous Father and as we request things that are in line with His Word, we can have confidence that He hears us and will grant us those petitions. On the other hand, God wants us to have pure motives, free from greed and selfishness when we are praying. It's important that our hearts are in tune with God and His Word and His will as we pray. This way we'll have pure motives and the desires of our hearts will also be His desire for us. Let's look at a few verses that talk to us about heart motives as we pray.

5.   James 4:2-3

God gives us some instructions about having selfish motives when we pray. What does this passage tell us about praying selfish, greedy prayers?

_____

MY STORY: *Let me give you an example. There are times that our kids want us to buy them certain things - teen stuff! Have you ever wanted your parents to buy you something? Sometimes, even though we wanted our children to have the things they desired, at that time we didn't have enough money to purchase it. We told our kids that they should pray about it and ask the Lord to provide it for them. We knew this would be a good chance for them to learn how to pray faith-filled prayers and a great opportunity for them to see how good and generous God is. Maybe you desire some things your parents cannot purchase for you right now. Maybe you desire new clothes? A car? Stereo or CD's? Computer? Here's a story of when our son was a pre-teen, perhaps it will inspire you to seek the Lord when your parents can't afford to purchase everything your heart desires. Before I tell you my story, let me remind you that it's important that you have a sincere and obedient heart toward God when you ask Him for things. Just like your parents, God does want to bless His children; but just like your parents, God is not interested in satisfying the desires of a whiney, spoiled, selfish child. He's listening for your childlike faith and thankfulness.*

LUKE'S STORY: *A few years ago, one of our sons, Luke, wanted a Game Boy. Again, at the time we couldn't afford to buy him a Game Boy, but we knew God had the ability to provide him with one. He had been living a life pleasing to the Lord, so I prayed with him* about this. We went to the Lord and we thanked Him for being a good God who gives good gifts. We asked the Lord for the Game Boy he wanted. We thanked the Lord by faith that He had heard our prayer and since we knew He heard us, we knew we had the Game Boy we requested. I told my son that from that point on, whenever he thought about the Game Boy he should just thank God for the game and in His timing, he would have it. I also challenged my son to think about giving something valuable to others as a seed sown into others' lives.

Do you want to know what happened? First, my son had been saving up "Bible Bucks" from church. This is "money" kids earn in Children's Church when they bring their Bibles to church, when they know their memory verses, etc. One day at church they received an offering for needy people and my son gave all of his Bible Bucks in that offering. Did he get the Game Boy right after giving away all his Bible Bucks? Nope! My son began to grow impatient as several months passed and there was no Game Boy. We just encouraged him to continue to thank God if he really believed that God had heard his original prayer, and that God was working on it. A few more months passed and no Game Boy! This was a real test of being thankful and patient! He continued to thank the Lord for his Game Boy even when he was feeling impatient! After about nine months had passed, guess what happened? One of the guest speakers we had at our church, who didn't know Luke, felt "impressed by God" to give him $100! This person didn't know what our son had prayed about! When Luke saw the $100 bill, his face lit up! That week he took that $100 God gave him and bought the Game Boy! God knows how to answer the prayers of young people! He is a good Father!

I hope you notice a few things from these stories. First, do you see the importance of having the right heart and attitude before God? Do you see the need to ask and have a thankful heart – even when you grow impatient? Do you see the importance of looking for ways to be a blessing and give to others when you are expecting God to bless you? Do you see the need to exercise your faith and be patient? Can you see that every situation is unique and God knows just how to answer your request?

D. When Should We Pray?

1.   1 Thessalonians 5:17

        When should we pray?_____

2.	Philippians 4:6-7

Are we supposed to worry?_____

What are we supposed to do when we are tempted to worry?_____

After we tell God our need, what are we supposed to do?_____

What will God do?_____

## E.	Who Should We Pray For?

1.	1 Timothy 2:1-4

Who should we pray for acccording to this passage?_____

Who is our President?_____

Who else is an authority over you?_____

_____

2.	Ephesians 6:18

Who should we pray for?_____

3.	Matthew 9:35-38

Jesus loves everyone so much! He doesn't want anyone to be hurting or lost without Him. When He looked at the world, He saw a garden of people ripe and ready, but something was wrong.

What was wrong?_____

What did Jesus tell us to pray for?_____

4. Luke 6:28

This is a challenge sometimes!

Who are we supposed to pray for?_____

Praying is such an honor! Just think, when you talk to your Heavenly Father and pray to Him about things and for people, He answers your prayer! Other people will be blessed because you prayed. Your own life will be blessed because you prayed. Maybe you will want to make a list of people you have on your heart to pray for. Can you think of five people in your heart you would like to pray for?

Write down their names:

_____

F. What Messes Up Our Prayers?

Sometimes we need to make an adjustment in our hearts for our prayers to work the way God wants. Let's look at a few things the Lord tells us.

1. Psalm 66:18-19

What makes God not listen to our prayers?_____

If we confess our sins and make a decision to stop sinning in a given area, God will hear our prayers! But, if we want to keep on sinning, God will not be able to answer our prayers. This is really important. If you think that you can seek God's answers to your prayers while at the same time living a life of being sassy and disobedient to your parents, disrespectful, loose with your words, partying, sleeping with your girlfriend or boyfriend or engaging in any type of premarital sex, being rebellious in your attitude rather than teachable or submissive, if you violate your own conscience by watching movies, videos, tv programs, going to internet sites or listening to music that your own heart tells you is wrong, you are totally kidding yourself. God expects you as a young person to be a Christian in these areas. If you blow it and sin, then you need to ask God to forgive you and you may need to ask your parents or others to forgive you, too. Then God will be able to answer your prayers. Sin is the biggest hinderance to having your prayers answered.

2.   Mark 11:25

When we are praying, what are we supposed to do if we have a grudge or unforgiveness towards someone?

_____

Did you know that you will feel guilty inside your heart if you have been disobedient to your parents, fought with your friends, brothers or sisters, have been mouthy to others, had a moody, bad attitude, or held a grudge against someone? Has anyone ever done something to you that totally hurt your feelings? What if they made fun of you? Have you ever not been included or invited to a party or a get together with friends? How did you feel? Have you ever been jealous of others? Envious? Have you secretly hoped that things didn't work out for someone because you were offended by them? These types of things will cause a root of bitterness and unforgivenss to lodge in your heart, and it will hinder God from being able to work in your life and answer your prayers. If you were honest, you would notice that there is a scratchy feeling in your conscience. What do you need to do when things like this happen? First, talk to the Lord and apologize to Him. Second, forgive anyone who has done you wrong and be sure to apologize to anyone you have been mean or disobedient toward. Once you forgive and apologize, your heart will feel so much better and God will be able to answer your prayers.

Prayer is an awesome privilege! We get to talk to the God of the universe and He answers! Have you ever thought of keeping a prayer diary or prayer journal? You'll see an example of one in the "Real Christians Do It" section.

You might want to start keeping a Prayer Diary or a Prayer Journal where you can write letters of prayer to the Lord. Have you ever written a letter to the Lord? All you need is a pen and a notebook and you can begin!

MY STORY: *I kept a journal when I was first a Christian. Each day I would write a short letter to the Lord to praise and thank Him for blessing my life, to ask Him for help in specific areas of my life, and to pray for the people He had put on my heart. When I was 19 years old and a student in college, I started writing letters to the Lord in my journal. Here is one of the first letters I wrote to the Lord when I was just a baby Christian.*

Winter 1978

Dear God,

Hi, this sure feels funny writing to You. Ok, first I want to clear up some things. I'm really deeply sorry for my sins and You know what they are. Even my thoughts sometimes I'm sorry for. I want to thank You for all the things you have given and shown me...Please help me to become a better person. I really want to be able to know You better and show Your love. Also, just be with me through my finals – especially chemistry! Also guide me through my college life and this summer. Thank You for everything.

I love You!

Beth

It's a pretty simple letter, but writing letters like this over the past 25 years has helped me get to know God better. It's a great way to write down your prayers for others, and when you read your journal you will be really happy to see how well you are getting to know the Lord.

How does God talk to you? Will you hear his voice out of heaven? Probably not! God talks to His children through the Bible. God's Word, the Bible, is God's personal love letter to you. As you read the Bible, you will sense that God Himself is whispering in your spiritual ear. The Bible is unlike any other book because it is alive and full of life and power.

MY STORY: *I remember when I first started reading the Bible. The Bible was different than any other book I had read. It seemed to be alive! It wasn't a boring schoolbook or just facts on a page; it seemed like God was sitting on my shoulder and talking to my heart as I read the Bible!*

Just like you eat food every day for your body to grow strong, you need to eat spiritual food every day, too. When you read your Bible it's just like eating spiritual food for your spirit to grow strong. Since the Bible will give you spiritual food, strength, light and power, the devil will do anything he can to distract you from reading it. Your Bible will teach you everything you need to know about how to walk in God's blessings in this life. It is no wonder Satan fights so hard to keep you from reading it! If you will read your Bible every day, God will show you many things about His love and all that He has planned for your life.

Let's look at this exciting Book!

A.   Who Wrote The Bible?

1.   2 Timothy 3:16

Who inspired men to write all that is in the Bible?_____

2.   John 5:39

Jesus told us what the main theme of the Bible is.

Who do the Scriptures tell us about?

_____

B.   How Long Will God's Word Be True?

1.   Matthew 24:35

How long will God's Words last?_____

2.   1 Peter 1:25

How long will God's Word last?_____

3.   Isaiah 40:8

The flowers and grass will turn brown and wither away, but what will God's Word do?

_____

THE BIBLE IS A SUPERNATURAL BOOK: Did you know the Bible is unlike any other Book in history? It is alive! The Bible was written by forty different men who had different careers. Some were fisherman, some were farmers, some were doctors, some were kings and some were preachers – God used forty different people that had different kinds of jobs to write His Words. It took 1500 years to write the Bible. God used people from different generations to write His Words! It was written in three different languages – Hebrew, Aramaic and Greek. Today, we read our whole Bible in English, but it was originally written in these three languages. The Bible has one central theme – Jesus Christ is the star of every part of the Bible. It is obvious that there was really One Supreme Author – God, the Holy Spirit, was in charge of writing the Bible!

C.   How Does God's Word Help Us?

1.   2 Timothy 3:16,17

God's Word is useful to help us know what is _____

What does God's Word tell us about our lives?_____

2.   Hebrews 4:12

How sharp is God's Word?_____

48

What does it do in our hearts?_____

3.   Psalm 119:11, 105

If we hide God's Word in our hearts, how does that help us?_____

How does God's Word help us walk in God's paths?_____

4.   Psalm 119:103

What does God's Word taste like to our hearts?_____

5.   Matthew 4:4

What do we need to eat if we want to have a strong life with God?_____

6.   Luke 8:4-15

This is the story of the "sower and the seed". Jesus is showing us how God's Word is like a seed and our hearts are like the ground. He describes four different types of soil or hearts. Can you describe what happened to the seed of God's Word that was planted in these four hearts?

The Hard Path:_____

The Rocky Soil:_____

The Thorny Soil:_____

The Good Soil:_____

D.   What Are We Supposed To Do With God's Word?

1.   Colossians 3:16

Where is God's Word supposed to live?_____

It is our job to read the Bible so that God's Word fills our heart completely!

Have you ever seen your mom cook with a crock pot? A crock pot is a big electric ceramic pot that slowly cooks food. The process of slow cooking allows the rich flavors of each food in the crock pot to come out which makes the finished product very tasty! For example, if you cut up various vegetables and chunks of steak mixed with a rich beef broth, a crock pot will make the best beef stew you've ever had! Did you know that your heart is like a big crock pot? God's Word is like the vegetables and chunks of steak. The rich beef broth is like the work of the Holy Spirit. If you'll take the time to read God's Word in small and big chunks and allow it to settle into the crock pot of your heart, the Holy Spirit will slow cook it over time and He'll water it with His tasty broth, so that after a while you will have tasty "Holy Ghost Word stew" dwelling richly in your heart! The good news is that any time you need something to eat spiritually, you'll be able to dish up a bowl of stew to feed yourself, and better yet, you'll have something to feed the people in your life that are hungry for God! It's so important to spend time in God's Word and let it dwell richly in you!

2.   2 Timothy 2:15

As we grow and learn God's Word, what does God want us to be able to do?

_____

3.   Joshua 1:8

How often are we to study and think about God's Word in our lives?_____

When we know God's Word and obey it, what does He promise?_____

4.   James 1:21-25

After we hear God's message, what are we to do with it?_____

What happens if we hear God's Word, but we do not obey it?_____

What happens if we hear God's Word, and we do obey it?_____

E.   Who Helps Us Understand The Word?

Your parents, pastor, youth leaders or other Christians may help teach you the Bible, but the best Teacher of all is the Holy Spirit. He will speak directly to your heart as you read the Bible. Let's look at this.

John 14:23-26

Who will teach us and remind us of everything Jesus tells us in the Word?_____

YOU'VE GOT MAIL: Do you enjoy getting email or instant messages? Do you spend a lot of time talking with your friends through the internet? There is something fun and quite amazing about the fact that you can talk to your friends on line, no matter where in the world they live! I've noticed that my kids and most other teens have their own internet language. One day I was looking over my daughter Annie's shoulder and saw her write: "pos". Of course, I had to ask her what that meant! She let me know it meant, "parent over shoulder"...and it was time for me to let her and her friends talk without my interference! Did you know that the Bible is God's language? When you and I read the Bible, the Holy Spirit downloads God's message to our heart. It's as if heaven says, "you've got mail" before we open our Bibles. If you will trust God and read your Bible with an expectant heart you'll be thrilled to receive "instant messages" from God through His Word. He will quicken or cause a Scripture to "jump off the page" and speak directly to your heart. God's Word is alive - it's living and active! The Holy Spirit makes it very present tense, and God can literally send you an "instant message"everytime you read your Bible.

Let's look at some practical ways we can study the Bible in the "Real Christians Do It" section.

Now it's time to just do it! Let's take action on what we've studied. Look up this passage.

2 Timothy 3:14-15

Timothy was a young man when the Apostle Paul wrote him the letters 1 Timothy and 2 Timothy. Notice what Paul said about Timothy in verse 15.

When was Timothy taught the Scriptures; the Bible?_____

What did it do for him?_____

Why not decide right now that you will spend the first 5-10 minutes of the day reading your Bible? Or maybe you can spend the last 5-10 minutes of the day, right before you go to sleep, reading your Bible. Talk to your parents to develop a plan for your Bible reading and learning. Be sure to include things like going to church regularly, maybe listening to the Bible on CD, listening to other teaching materials and reading books and autobiographies that will boost your faith.

Teens can learn, know and grow from reading the Bible. God will talk to you through His Word and lead you in the way He has for you. If you will put God's Word first in your life – if you will expect God to speak to your heart and if you will obey what He tells you – you will live a life blessed by God!

I want to challenge you to read through the entire Bible, at least once, by the time you graduate from high school. Here are some ideas on how you can have fun reading your Bible. Why don't you pick one and get started?

1.   Read Proverbs each month - by reading just 1 chapter in Proverbs each day!
2.   Read Psalms each month - by reading just 5 Psalms each day!
3.   Read the "Go Eat Pop Corn" books - by reading Galatians, Ephesians, Philippians & Colossians.
4.   Read the Old & New Testaments - by reading just 1 chapter in each testament each day.
5.   Read the Gospel of Matthew in a week - by reading just 4 chapters each day!
6.   Read the Book of Acts in a week - by reading just 4 chapters each day.
7.   Read the Gospel of John and 1st, 2nd, and 3rd John in 1 week - by reading just 4 chapters each day.
8.   EXTREME CHRISTIANS: Read the entire New Testament in 26 days - by reading 10 chapters a day!

God wants your life to be blessed. Did you know there is a life God blesses? You probably also know people who are not living a very blessed life. All of us can grow in our walk and obedience to God and we'll find more and more of His blessing in our lives! Who's living the blessed life? It's the person who trusts the Lord and obeys the Lord. Sure, you may face trials and tests at times, but if you'll listen to the Lord and obey Him and His Word, in the end you will be a blessed person. He has promised us that He will help us through any difficulty and that He will bless our lives as we obey Him and follow His directions.

A.   Why Should We Obey God And Follow Him?

1.   1 John 4:8

   What does this verse tell us about God – God is_____

   Since God is love, it is easy to obey Him! We don't have to be afraid of obeying God – we can trust Him and obey because He loves us more than anyone else does and wants the very best for us. For some reason, some people are afraid to obey God because they think He'll ruin their lives or make their lives really boring, or maybe He'll send them to some remote jungle of the world to be a missionary! God is love and He wants the best for you. Trust Him!

2.   John 14:15

   How do we show God that we love Him?_____

3.   John 14:21,23,24

   According to these verses, who really loves God?_____

   If a person says he loves God, but doesn't obey God, what do you think that means?

   _____

B.   What Does God Want Us To Obey?

Did you know that there is really only one command God wants us to obey? Really. Jesus said it plainly! He said the greatest commandment was to be a lover! We are to love God and to love others. Sounds simple, right? Did you know if we obey this one command, we will be obeying all the other commands of the Bible? Think about this. Do you love God? Do you love others? Let's look at this "law of love"that God wants us to follow.

1.   John 13:34,35

    Who are we supposed to love?_____

    What does our love prove?_____

2.   Matthew 22:36-40

    What is the most important command God gave us?_____

3.   Romans 13:10

    If we love others, what will we never do?_____

4.   John 15:12-17

    What is the greatest way to show others you love them?_____

    What do you think that means in every day life?_____

D.   What Happens When We Obey God?

Obedience makes or breaks true Christians! Obedience separates the men from the boys! Your obedience to God will determine in large part how blessed your life is. As a young person, make the decision to be quick to obey God in any area of your life He speaks to you about. We'll see this truth in several Scriptures.

1.   Luke 6:46-49

Read the story and place an "x" in the column that answers the question.

	Obedient	Disobedient
Who heard what Jesus said?		
Who obeyed God's Words?		
Who faced a storm?		
Whose house fell?		
Whose house stood firm?		

What is the only difference between the person whose house stood strong and the person whose house fell apart?

_____

2.   Isaiah 1:19

If we are willing and obedient, what does God promise us?_____

E.   The First And Primary Commandment: Obey Your Parents

When you are a young person, God wants you to obey and honor your parents. This should be one of the priorities of every teenager. Did you know there are two good reasons to obey and honor your parents? First, God promises that things will go well for those who obey and honor their parents. Second, God promises long life on the earth to those children who obey and honor their parents. Make obeying and honoring your parents or guardians one of your number one goals!

God gave you parents to love you, nourish you and protect you. One of the quickest ways to get in the flow of God's blessings as a young person is to simply choose to obey and honor your parents. Some people have gotten in bad habits of arguing with, disrespecting, swearing or rolling their eyes at, being mouthy towards, being rude or hurtful and disobedient to their parents. If you want to get on God's "bad side" this is a quick way to do it! It's important that you obey God by obeying and honoring your parents.

Here's a little side note. Sometimes, young people have parents who are not Christians. What do you do in that case? You should still obey and honor your parents. However, if they ask you to do something that is illegal, immoral or contradictory to God's commands, then you need to obey God rather than your parents. These are difficult issues and it's always best to seek the counsel of a Christian leader or pastor who is more mature than you are so that they can help you make decisions that will still honor your parents. Let me share an example with you.

WHAT IF MY PARENTS AREN'T CHRISTIANS?: I once knew a teenage girl who was very troubled. She was in a public school, popular, a cheerleader and yet very mixed up. She had started to hang out with a group of kids that partied and she was being pressured to do things that she really didn't want to do. As a result, her friends started to make fun of her and she went into a serious depression. She was so depressed that she did not want to go to school anymore. I met her at about this time and through sharing God's Word and His love with her, she became a Christian and invited Jesus Christ to be the Lord of her life. Instantly I could see her eyes glisten and she displayed the first genuine, heartfelt smile I had ever seen in her! She was truly born again and very aware of God's love for her. She was hungry for God and His Word and began to attend our church and the "Getting A Grip On The Basics" class we offered.

Guess what happened? Her parents got very upset! They were "religious", but not born again and they didn't like the idea that their "popular, cheerleader daughter" was getting too on fire for the Lord. They told her she couldn't go to church anymore! They would rather have her be the popular cheerleader who was mixed up and depressed, than the glowing born-again Christian she had just become. They mocked her for reading her Bible. They called her a religous fanatic and really made it rough for her. Well, what was she to do? Obey her parents? Quit attending church and dry up spiritually? Honor her parents, yet not obey them in quitting church? In her case, she shared her heart with them in a mature way and honored them in her approach and she was able to convince them that it would be good for her to attend church. This was a difficult situation for her and she had to consistently choose to honor her parents when they made fun of her faith. She did her best to honor them by being obedient, working hard in school, keeping her room clean and doing many other things to demonstrate to her parents that her Christianity was a real thing for her. Can you see the difference beween obeying and honoring your parents if they ask you to go

56

against God's Word or His laws? If you are facing this type of situation, I want to encourage you to seek the counsel of your own pastor or youth leader.

1.   Ephesians 6:1-3

      Children, what does God want you to do?_____

      Why?_____

      What two things has God promised to those children who obey and honor their parents?

      _____   _____

      How would you define "obey"?_____

      How would you define "honor"?_____

      Would you like to live a long life?_____

      Would you like a life of blessing?_____

2.   Luke 2:41-52

      In verse 51, what did Jesus do?_____

3.   Proverbs 1:8-9

      Why should we listen to and obey our mom and dad?_____

F.   Obey God In These Areas

1.   Pick the Right Kind of Friends

      Did you know that God is interested in the people you choose as friends? God wants you to love everyone, but He doesn't want you to be friends with just anyone.

FRIENDS: Our friends are so important to us! As teenagers we make so many new friends and get close to them in school, on the internet and through hanging out. This is a very important part of being a teenager.

God is concerned about whom you choose for a friend and He has told us to choose friends that love Him. That's because He wants our lives to be blessed. You'll know all kinds of people, but you get to decide who you'll choose to be your friends. You've already met some kids who don't love God. You probably know some teens that rebel against their parents or some kids who like to swear, or steal, or look at perverse things on videos, in magazines or on the internet. You likely know people that listen to music with trashy lyrics and you know people that mock Christian music. You probably also know the young people that smoke cigarettes or pot, and the ones who like to drink beer and take drugs. Maybe there are some teens in your neighborhood or at school that do some of the things we mentioned. They might be nice people, just doing the wrong things.

What should you do? Ignore them? Be mean to them? Do what they do so you fit in? No! You should pray for them and be nice to them. Most of the time people do things that are wrong because no one has ever shown them that doing the right things can actually be cool and fun! It's very likely that the young people that do these types of things have never heard about a Jesus they can relate to. He's always been portrayed as the boring, mean, "take away all your fun" God - instead of the personal, caring, forgiving, full of real life God! Many times these teens have thought being a Christian meant you had to be a big geek and the dork of the school. Why don't you be the one to show them what a cool Christian looks like, without compromising! Make it your goal to be an example of a loving, friendly Christian that knows the real Jesus! Your life and lifestyle will preach to them in a way they can see!

In the meantime, look for other friends who share your love for the Lord. Sometimes this is hard to do, especially if you are not in a Christian school. Pray and ask God to send you a Christian friend or send you the type of friends that are open to Him. When you meet friends that are open to God, you will have the opportunity to witness to them and you could be the one to lead them to the Lord! It's important that you seek Christian friends so that you have people to talk to and pray with. Christian friends will not try to influence you away from the Lord, but they will support your Christian lifestyle. As a teenager, these types of friends are really important.

1 Corinthians 15:33

How would you describe people that are "bad company"?_____

2.   Keep Your Heart Pure

Proverbs 4:22

What does God want us to do with our hearts?_____

Why is it important to keep a pure heart in God's sight?_____

What type of standards do you have regarding movies? music? video/dvds? internet sites? Does your own conscience bother you if you view things that are ungodly?

_____

What would you do if you were at a movie theatre or a friend's house and an ungodly, immoral, sexually perverse or evil movie was showing?

_____

What would you do if your friend asked you to look at a pornographic internet site or magazines with him or her?

_____

Can you see that it takes guts and courage to be a Christian? _____

You can't be a wimpy, "follow the crowd", everyone-has-to-like-me type of person if you are going to be a Christian.

3.   Speak Good Words

Ephesians 4:29

What kind of words did God say we shouldn't use?_____

What kind of words does God want us to use?_____

What kind of words does this eliminate from your vocabulary?_____

Besides swear words, what types of words should you eliminiate?_____

Remember, God wants you to obey Him for your own benefit! He has a life that is blessed for each one of us to enjoy and as we obey His Word, we will continue to place ourselves in position to walk in God's very best!

Also remember this: make obedience your goal, but if and when you blow it, God is full of mercy and forgiveness. In the next chapter we'll look at God's love and forgiveness.

When we think about obeying God it's important to evaluate how you are doing. In the "Real Christians Do It" section, let's think about the relationship you have with your parents and what you can do to honor and obey them.

Let's take action on what we've studied. I want to encourage you to be quick to obey God's Word by loving God and loving others and by obeying your parents. If you will learn this as a child, you will save yourself from difficulties later in life and you will enjoy a peaceful life with God's blessings.

Think about your own relationship with your parents. What are some ways you can be more obedient to your parents? What are some ways you can show them the honor they deserve?

_____

_____

I know that you will make a good decision to do your best to obey God. However, sometimes we make mistakes. Can you think of areas where you have been disobedient? In our next chapter, we'll discuss how to obtain God's forgiveness.

Let's take a few minutes to look up this prayer in Colossians 1:9-10 and let's pray it for ourselves now!

Dear Father,

I pray and ask You to fill me with the knowledge of Your will. Give me spiritual wisdom and understanding. I pray that I may live a life pleasing to You in every way. I pray I bear fruit in every good work and that I grow in my knowledge of You. Help me to obey you Lord. Help me to obey and honor my parents. Help me to be the Christian You have called me to be. In Jesus' Name. Amen.

Have you ever blown it? Messed up? Disobeyed? Made a mistake? We all have. When we blow it, mess up, or make a mistake – we have sinned. If we are honest, our hearts begin to condemn us and we feel guilty. Sometimes, we cover our guilty feelings up with anger, frustration and depression. Enough of these negative feelings and we can get to the point that we actually feel sick. If we don't deal with the guilt we experience when we sin, we will feel far away from God.

MY STORY: *I remember when I was in 9th grade I messed up big time! One night my girlfriends and I had a sleepover, slumber party at Linda's house. We were sleeping outside in her backyard and at about midnight we got a stupid brilliant idea! We decided to do two things we should not have done. First, we wanted to "toilet paper" the "rich" neighborhood across the street. Second, we wanted to "streak" across the main road in our town at about 2am. Really dumb teen stuff.*

So, to begin with all 13 of us snuck up to the local Burger King where we stole every roll of toilet paper they had in both the men's and women's rooms! Then we went to the convenience store next door and bought another dozen rolls of toilet paper. We made our way back to the "rich" neighborhood to begin the party! Well, we decorated that neighborhood good...we had toilet paper everywhere. A few of our boyfriends decided to join in and they threw firecrackers in the bushes of people's homes. Can you believe this?

Well, after we had thoroughly decorated the neighborhood, we snuck back to our sleepover. On the way back to Linda's house we noticed a car coming down the road with its search lights on. Oh no...we realized it was the police, so we all scurried and hid behind houses, bushes, cars, anywhere we could be invisible! The police didn't see us and we made it back to Linda's safely with our adrenaline pumping! Within about 10 minutes of our "safe" return, the police pulled up. They walked over to our sleepover and began to question our evening activities. Of course, we denied everything, and acted like innocent teenage girls who were just having a slumber party. The policemen left and we sighed a big relief!

Within a few hours, we were feeling brave again and this is when some of the girls decided to "streak" across the main street. Two of the girls were going to be the "streakers" while the rest of us cheered them on. Just about the time the streakers had gotten enough courage to do it, the police pulled up again. We were busted! We began walking in the other direction when one of the officers said to all 13 of us girls, "Get in the car!" How could all 13 of us get in the car? We kept on walking and he barked again, "I said 'get in the car'." We all stopped and one by one we squished into the policeman's car. As the policeman took us back to Linda's house, I thought my life was over. I was sure that my mother would kill me. How could we be so stupid? Now, I was in big trouble!

Well, the end of the story is that the police let us off with a warning and my mother didn't kill me. I realized years later that it was God's pure mercy given to me "on credit" that saved my life.

When I finally gave my heart to Jesus years later, I was so thankful that He forgave me of doing all the stupid things we did as teenagers.

MY STORY: *When I was 18 years old and attending college, I remember one day I made a deal with God. Have you ever made a deal with the Lord? If He would protect you or get your out of a big mess, you promised that you would try to be a good person? Well, one day after Christmas break my parents were driving me back to college. It was about an hour drive and that particular day the roads were a complete sheet of ice. We were in the middle of a blizzard and the van we were in just slid all over the highway. It was so scary. I really thought we were not going to make it. When I looked out the window and saw our van skating from left to right I just knew we were going to die! I remember I just closed my eyes and prayed, "Dear God...if you will let us live and not slide off the road I promise I will quit smoking." I was making a deal with God! Well, the story ends with me making it safely to my dorm room, but guess what? I did not quit smoking! I did not hold up my end of the bargain until one and a half years later! I was so glad for God's mercy. He kept His side of the deal, but I did not. Even still, He was so merciful to protect me and within that next year I finally discovered how I could know Him personally as I became a Christian. Shortly after I became a Christian, I wanted to honor and obey the Lord and I quit smoking.*

Here's a story that will help us to understand how much God loves us and how much He wants to help us when we blow it!

WHAT WOULD YOU DO? Suppose you were riding your bike or maybe you just borrowed your parents car and were returning home. What if, as you were entering the garage, your bike or side of the car accidently hit, scraped and slighty dented your father's car? After you hit the car, you immediately check to see what kind of damage you have done. When you see the damage you don't know what to do. You are wrestling with the question, "Should I tell dad?" You decide that you aren't going to say anything about it to your dad. If you don't tell your dad what you did, maybe your dad will assume that something else hit his car. Maybe he'll think the door of another car scratched his car while he was parked at work or something like that. Besides, if you did tell your dad, maybe you would get in trouble, be grounded or lose the privilege of using your bike, or of borrowing the car for a while. What you don't know is that your dad saw the whole thing. He opened the garage door to take out the trash and he watched you slide right into his car. He saw you check the damage – he saw it all! At dinner, your dad is waiting for you to tell him what happened. When you don't say anything, how do you think that affects your relationship with him?

How do you think the dad feels?_____

Do you think the father and the child are feeling close to one another right now?_____

What should the kid do if he wants to feel close to his father again?_____

Do you think the father still loves his child?_____

Our relationship with our Heavenly Father is similar to our relationship with our earthly fathers. Our heavenly Father knows everything we think and He sees everything we do. God loves us and is willing to forgive us if we will be honest and confess our sins to Him.

What does God want us to do when we mess up, do mean things or disobey Him?_____

Will God help us to experience His love and forgiveness?_____

A. What Is Sin?

Sin is when we disobey God or we disobey our parents and even our own hearts. These verses tell us how God defines sin.

1.   James 4:17

     What is a sin?_____

65

2.   Romans 14:23

If you do anything you think is not right, you are_____

B.   Who Sins?

1.   Romans 3:23

Who has sinned?_____

2.   1 John 1:8,10

If we say we have not sinned, what are we doing?_____

If we claim we have not sinned, what are we calling God?_____

C.   God Tells Us Not To Sin

1.   1 Corinthians 15:34

God wants us to stop_____

2.   James 1:13-16

Who never tempts us to sin?_____

Where does temptation come from?_____

TEMPTATION: It is important to remember that temptation is not sin. To be
tempted is normal for a Christian. Thoughts, ideas, imaginations, reasonings,
pretentions, arguments and ultimately strongholds aimed at our thinking,
weaknesses or lusts are what the devil uses to try to tempt us. Jesus was tempted by
the devil, and yet He never sinned. When you are tempted, don't let the enemy make
you feel as if you have already sinned. Resist the temptation and you will not sin.
Someone once said, you can't stop a bird from flying over your head, but you can stop
it from building a nest in your hair. Temptation is like that bird flying overhead.
When you resist the temptation it can't build a nest in your hair!

D.   How Can We Resist The Temptation To Sin?

1 Corinthians 10:13

Are the temptations you face different than what others face?_____

What will God do for you when you are tempted?_____

My daughter, Meghan, has grown up in a Christian home as a pastor's kid and she's faced temptations like any Christian teenager. Here's her story.

MEGHAN'S STORY: *I've been a PK (pastor's kid) all of my life, and so far it hasn't been that bad. When I was four years old I asked Jesus to be the Lord of my life. I don't really remember doing it, but I am glad to have known Jesus for almost all of my life. One of the tough things about my life has been school. I do great in grades and sports, and I have a lot of friends who respect me for who I am and what I stand for, but there are some people in school who choose to ignore or make fun of me because of my beliefs. I used to hate walking down the school halls being known as the girl in school who was the "goody goody", but as the years have gone by people have started to totally respect me for who I am. I'm not the "goody, goody" anymore and I feel that I have an impact on people, even if I haven't ever talked to them.*

Recently, my mom taught the "Getting A Grip On The Basics" class on television, and because of that a lot of people have said to me, "Hey, I saw your mom on TV," or "Why was your mom on TV?" Hearing that kind of stuff helps me to reach out to certain kids at school, by telling them what her program is all about.

Being a Christian at school isn't as easy as it would seem. I still face a lot of temptation, whether it's to cuss (which I know we all slip sometimes), cheat, lie, make a bad choice, and in some situations I even feel like I have to deny my faith to fit in, but I know that fitting in for one day at school isn't as important as receiving God's blessings now, and the one's I will get eternally. Remembering God has a plan for my life and that He is with me everyday no matter where I am helps me to conquer the temptations. I pray that this book will be a tool for you to use in your everyday life, even if you haven't known Jesus for all of your life. Let God's light shine through you so you can be a witness to those around you.

E. What Do We Do If We Sin?

Always remember that God loves you and He is always there for you to turn to and talk to when you make a mistake or mess up. Don't ever run from Him, but run <u>to</u> Him with your problems. He is the one who has all the answers and who will give you forgiveness.

1 John 1:9

This verse has been called the Christian's "bar of soap".

What are we supposed to do when we sin?_____

When we confess our sins to God – that means we tell God the sin or sins we have done - we let Him know that we agree with Him that what we did or failed to do was a sin.

After we confess our sins, what will God do?_____

What does God cleanse us from?_____

F. Where Does Sin Go?

1. Hebrews 8:12 and Hebrews 10:17

   The Lord will not_____ our sins.

2. Micah 7:19

   God will throw our sins into_____

G. A Story Of A Sinful Son And A Forgiving Father

Luke 15:11-32

Jesus told us the story of a boy who left home and went into the world to party, waste his money and live an ungodly life. He no longer wanted to be with his father, but chose to do things he knew were not right. He thought it would be fun to sin. The Bible says that sin is pleasurable, for a season. (Hebrews 11:25) But when the season is up, there is a rude awakening. After a while this boy found out that it wasn't fun to sin...he was broke, he had to eat the food that pigs eat, he didn't have any real friends and he was lonely. He wanted to go back home, but he didn't know what his father would think. He decided to go home and confess his sins to his father. When he arrived home, he told his dad that he had sinned and he was very sorry. Let's look at this story.

In verse 21, what did the son tell his father he'd done?_____

In verse 20, was the father glad that his son had come home?_____

What did the father do when he saw his son?_____

In verses 22-24, was the son treated like a sinner, a son or a servant?_____

Just think, that's how your Heavenly Father feels about you when you sin. Always remember to run quickly to the Lord, tell him you are sorry, and then thank Him for forgiving you. Remember that you are still a special son or daughter that He loves very much.

H.   A Look At Temptations And Real Life Issues

Let's talk about very practical areas of life. Habits. Attitudes. Associations. Lifestyles. Did you know that these things are important? The habits you develop – what you eat, drink, smoke and say – will either glorify God or they won't. The type of people you associate with will affect you in either a positive, godly way or in a negative, ungodly way. Your lifestyle – places you frequent, videos you watch, music you listen to, internet sites you visit – these are all indicators of your heart condition. Your sexual identity and purity matter. Do your habits, associations and lifestyle choices glorify God? Is it your heart's desire to overcome any stronghold that may have a grip in your life, so that you may glorify God in your entire life?

Did you know that as you grow as a Christian and as you increase in your service to God, you lose options? As a Christian who wants to honor God, you lose the option to "flesh out", to have temper tantrums, to have pity parties, to have fits of jealousy, to make excuses for ungodly habits and to live a carnal, undisciplined life. Honoring and obeying God means that you also lose your right to hold onto certain habits and lifestyles. God loves you, but as you mature and serve Him with your life, He expects you to grow up and to live a truly dedicated life. Let's look at this very practical subject.

When you are a teenager, often because your hormones are going in so many directions, you will face sexual temptations. Perhaps you've been tempted and sinned in any of the following areas: having sex before you are married, masturbating and arousing yourself sexually, engaging in homosexual activity, participating in oral sex or feeding on pornography. The good news is that if you will tell the Lord about your sin and make a decision to repent or stop doing it, He will forgive you and give you the power to keep yourself pure sexually. It's one of the best gifts you can give to your future spouse!

We live in a permissive and promiscuous society where people often justify behavior in relative terms, rather than living by God's Word and His absolutes. In the Christian and church world, as people are born again and begin growing in their walk and service to God, they often find the areas of drinking, smoking, foul language, premarital or extramarital sex, divorce and remarriage, homosexuality, gambling, movie and video choices, music preferences and the like become real heart issues that must be addressed. If you are dealing with any of these areas and struggling in any way, I encourage you to speak with your pastor or one of the church leaders for their spiritual guidance and encouragement. Let's look at several verses of Scripture which speak to these subjects in a general way.

1.　　Lifestyle Issues

　　　a.　　1 Corinthians 6:12; 10:23-24

　　　　　　What do these verses describe?_____

　　　b.　　Colossians 1:10, 1 Thessalonians 2:12

　　　　　　What type of life are we supposed to live? _____

　　　　　　_____

　　　c.　　1 Corinthians 10:31

　　　　　　What are we supposed to do in our eating, drinking and lifestyle?

　　　　　　_____

　　　d.　　1 Thessalonians 5:22

　　　　　　What are we to avoid?_____

70

e.   Psalms 101

How did the writer say he would live in his home?_____

What would he not set before his eyes? _____

What type of people would he not associate with? _____

f.   Romans 14:21

What should we do so that we don't cause our fellow Christian to stumble?

_____

2.   Clothing and How You Dress

a.   1 Timothy 2:9

How does God want us to dress?_____

How would you define "modest"?_____

b.   Romans 14:21

In what ways could our clothing cause others to stumble?_____

_____

There is a great passage in 1 Peter 3:3-4, which says, *"Don't be concerned about the outward beauty that depends on fancy hairstyles, expensive jewelry, or beautiful clothes. You should be known for the beauty that comes from within, the unfading beauty of a gentle and quiet spirit, which is so precious to God."* (NLT) God wants all of us to dress in an appropriate, modest way. That doesn't mean you have to wear a burlap bag and be the biggest geek in school. It means that we shouldn't wear clothes that are too tight, too low, too high, too revealing just be fashionable and modest. It's possible! If you will simply dress in a way that honors the Lord and in a way that doesn't cause others to stumble, you can still be cool and up to date with your clothing.

3.   Drinking And Partying Issues

    a.   Luke 21:34, Romans 13:13, Galatians 5:19-21, 1 Peter 4:2-5, Proverbs 31:4-6

        What do these verses say about getting drunk? _____

        How do these verses describe God's view of ungodly partying? _____

        While people debate whether Jesus turned the water at the wedding in Cana into real, alcoholic wine, it is clear that Jesus and the whole of Scripture clearly teach against drunkeness and living the ungoldy, immoral party life.

    b.   Proverbs 31:4-6

        What does this passage tell us about drinking for those who are in leadership?

        _____

        If you're a leader, class officer, student senate representative, captain of the team, supervisor at work, a leader of any kind, think about the power of your example on others. Whether you like it or not, when you are a leader you are a role model and people are looking to you. Be a real leader and show your friends that you don't have to drink to have fun. In fact, show them that you don't need to get high on drugs and alcohol, because as a Christian full of God you are happy with the Most High!

    c.   Ephesians 5:18

        What are not to be drunk with?_____

        What are we to be drunk (filled, intoxicated, under the influence) with?

        _____

Did you know that drinking and getting drunk on alcohol and drugs is the counterfeit to the real? God always has the real thing and the devil always tries to come up with the fake alternative. When you are under the influence or intoxicated with alchohol

72

and drugs it is the devil's substitution for the joy of really being under God's influence and intoxicated with the Holy Spirit. When you are filled with the Holy Spirit you can actually get quite happy! (Acts 2:1-21) You will find yourself feeling free, unhibited, bold and often full of laughter and joy! The good news is that it's not illegal and you won't have a hangover!

4.   Sexual Issues

    a.   1 Corithians 6:18, Ephesians 5:3-5, 1 Thessalonians 4:3-7

       What does God say about sleeping around and sexual relations outside of marriage?

       _____

    b.   Romans 1:21-32, 1 Corinthians 6:9-11,

       How do these passages describe God's view of homosexuality? _____

       _____

    c.   Romans 13:14, 2 Timothy 2:22, Jude 16-19

       What does the Bible say about lust – pornography and perversion?_____

       _____

Finally, let's talk about one more sexually-related subject that has affected many young girls. Teen pregnancy and the scars that having an abortion leave can run deep for many, many years.

WHAT IF SHE HAD AN ABORTION? Years ago, I knew a young girl who had had an abortion. She had suffered for years with a silent guilt. One day as she and I were talking about God and His work in her life, the Lord told me that this girl had had an abortion when she was younger. He let me know that she had accepted God's forgiveness, but she was having a hard time forgiving herself. In a gentle way, I told her what the Lord told me and she began to cry and and then she told me the story. I told her that while she had accepted God's forgiveness, she had not forgiven herself, but now it was time to do that. With a heart that was truly sorry, and with many repentant tears she came to the place where she was able to forgive herself for the sin of commiting abortion. If you've been sexually active, become pregnant and perhaps had an abortion, you need to know that if your heart is full of godly sorrow leading you to repentance, the Lord wants to forgive you and cleanse you from all unrighteousness, and He wants you to forgive yourself. When you receive God's forgiveness you are free to live a pure, godly life.

God loves everyone, sinner and saint alike! He loves the fornicator, the adulterer, the porn addict and the homosexual, and yet He has given us His will concerning our sexuality in His Word. As a young person make every effort to guard yourself by staying sexually pure. Don't allow your mind to feed on internet sites, videos, magazines, books or anything else that would paint unwholesome, perverted, inappropriate images of sex, your body, marriage or God's plan for your future. If you have already blown it in this area - then with true godly sorrow and a contrite heart, ask God to forgive you and to cleanse you; then forgive yourself and determine in the future that you will walk in purity. If we want to walk in God's blessings, we must make the choice to resist any and all sexual temptations and align our lives with His Word.

Maybe this would be a good time to evaluate your habits, attitudes, lifestyle, associations and perhaps repent. Are you willing to consecrate your entire life, spirit, soul and body to the Lordship of Jesus and His Word? As you think about your heart and actions in the area of being a servant, a good steward and a faithful person, do you see room for improvement? Why not pray a prayer like this from your heart and write down the actions and adjustments you plan to make.

"Dear Father God, I am so thankful that I can come boldly to Your throne of grace to obtain mercy and find grace to help me in my time of need. I recognize the areas of my life where I have sinned, where I have not followed Your will, where I have displeased You and I repent and turn 180 degrees from: (list the area or areas that God has dealt with your heart) _____ _____. I am sorry for sinning against You and others, I ask You to forgive me and to cleanse me from all unrighteousness, and I ask You for Your grace to help me walk in a manner worthy of You, fully pleasing to You. Thank You Father for Your forgiveness and Your grace to help. In Jesus' Name. Amen."

If you are looking for additional support and help, we have listed various resources. Please keep in mind, these resources represent various philosophies and doctrinal backgrounds and beliefs and you will need to use your own good judgment on which ones would be beneficial to you.

<u>For Various Links To Christian Support Resources:</u>
http://www.hoyweb.com/lh/support.htm
http://www.porn-free.org/links.htm

<u>For Alcohol-Related Issues:</u>
Alcoholics Anonymous: www.alcoholics-anonymous.org
Al-Anon: www.al-anon.org
Alcoholics Victorious: http://www.crc.iugm.org

<u>For Homosexual-Related Issues:</u>
http://www.exodusnorthamerica.org
Exodus International North America, Phone: 888-264-0877

<u>For Gambling-Related Issues:</u>
Gamblers Anonymous: www.gamblersanonymous.org

Now it's time to just do it! Let's take action on what we've studied. It's so important to keep an honest and pure heart before God. If you will confess your sins to Him when you blow it, you will enjoy a loving friendship with the Lord.

Maybe it would be helpful for you to take a moment to do just what 1 John 1:9 tells us to do.

- On a piece of paper, why don't you write down any sins that you have done that you have not already confessed to the Lord.

- Once you've written them down, look up 1 John 1:9 and read it out loud.

- After you have read it, write "1 John 1:9" in big letters across that piece of paper.

- Now say, "All of these sins are now forgiven, and I am cleansed from all wrong doing."

- Now, tear that piece of paper up into little, tiny pieces and throw those pieces away, never to be remembered!

This is exactly what God does with our sin when we confess it to Him. He will forgive us and remember them no more!

CHAPTER 8	**Being Filled With The Holy Spirit**
	"How To Experience God's Power"

Do you play sports? Have you watched athletes on television? Have you ever watched the Olympics? Have you noticed that when athletes are working really hard they sweat? They need to drink lots of water if they are going to be full of energy and strength in competition. Did you know this is true for Christians? We're like athletes for God! We are running in the Christian race! Every day we're training as we get to know God, as we pray to God, as we love people, and when we are running to tell as many people as we can about how they can know Jesus and go to heaven. It is so exciting to be an athlete for God! Sometimes we need a big drink of God's water so that we can be full of God's energy and strength. When we are filled with the Holy Spirit, it's like God is filling us up with His water so that we can run our race for Him full of power, energy and strength!

Do you remember when we talked about the Trinity or Godhead – God the Father, Jesus the Son and the Holy Spirit? Once we've asked Jesus into our hearts to be our Lord, the Bible calls us Christians or believers. We now have a Heavenly Father and Jesus as our friend. But more exciting things are in store for us. We have the opportunity to receive more of God in our lives. We can ask our Father and Jesus to fill us with His Holy Spirit. Would you like to be filled up with more of God? In some places in the Bible this is called being "filled with the Holy Spirit", "receiving the Holy Spirit" or "being baptized in the Holy Spirit".

Let's look in our Bibles to find out more.

A.   God Wants You To Be Full Of His Power

Acts 1:8

When the Holy Spirit fills you, what happens?_____

Why does God fill you with His power?_____

Have you ever told other people about Jesus?_____

Would you like God to give you power so that you can tell people about Jesus?_____

Someone once described being filled with the Spirit and the power that can come from our lives as being like taking a Coke can and shaking it up...and then opening the lid! Because the can is "full of Coke", Coke sprays all over the place! Jesus wants to "spray" from your life all over people, and He does this when you are filled with the Spirit!

B.   God Has A Gift For You

1.   Acts 2:38-39

Peter called the Holy Spirit a_____

Do you like gifts?_____

Who did Peter say this promised gift was for?_____

Does that include you?_____

Do you think God gives good gifts?_____

Aren't you glad that God said this gift was for children? _____

2.   Acts 1:4-5

What did Jesus tell His disciples they would be baptized with?_____

3.   Acts 2:4

When Jesus gave His disciples the gift of the Holy Spirit, what happened?_____

4.   Ephesians 5:18-20

What does God want His children to be filled with?_____

What does God not want His children to do?_____

When we are filled with the Spirit, what will we enjoy doing?_____

C.   Who Received This Gift In The Bible?

1.   Matthew 3:16

The Holy Spirit _____ on Jesus

2.   Acts 2:4

Everyone present was_____ with the Spirit

3.   Acts 8:17

These believers_____ the Holy Spirit

4.   Acts 9:17

Brother Saul was_____ with the Holy Spirit

5.   Acts 10:47

The Holy Spirit _____ on everyone who heard and received the message.

6.   Acts 19:6

When Paul laid hands on these disciples, the Holy Spirit_____ them.

D. You Can Receive God's Gift

1.   James 1:17

God gives us good and perfect gifts. This verse describes God's gifts as:

Whatever is _____ and _____ comes from God above.

2.   Luke 11:9-13

How do we obtain gifts from God?_____

List what the son did not expect to get when he asked his father for...

Bread – he did not expect_____

Fish – he did not expect_____

Egg – he did not expect_____

What will your Heavenly Father give you if you ask for the Holy Spirit?_____

E.   You Will Receive A Spiritual Language From God

Did you know that as a Christian you are like a special agent for God? You are on a mission and God gives you His energy and power to do your mission. Not only that, He gives you a special code language that only He understands! The Bible calls this speaking in tongues or speaking in the Spirit.

Have you ever wanted to have a secret language that you and your friends could use to talk to each other? It seems that young people have their own language on the internet and in instant messaging. When I was a kid, my sisters and I made up a special code language that no one but us could understand. It was called "jibberish". We could talk in complete sentences and our friends and even our parents couldn't figure out what we were saying! We had a lot of fun using this language to frustrate my mother!

Guess what? God wants you to have a special language so that you can talk and pray things to Him that the devil can't understand! You are God's secret agent and He has a special language just for you. It's a language, given by the Holy Spirit, that comes straight from your heart. Let's look at this.

1.   Acts 2:4

What could these believers do when they were filled with the Holy Spirit?_____

2.   Acts 10:45-46

When the Gentile believers were filled with the Spirit, what did they do?_____

3.   Acts 19:6

When the Holy Spirit filled these believers, what happened?_____

F.   How To Use Your Spiritual Language

God has given us the ability to speak from our hearts in tongues or spiritual language for a purpose! Why does God want us filled with the Spirit and speaking in tongues?

1.   1 Corinthians 14:2

Who are you talking to when you speak in tongues?_____

What are you speaking?_____

Notice that when you speak or pray in tongues, you are speaking not to men but to God. You are not speaking to the devil, but to God. You are speaking out mysteries. For example: Is your future a mystery to you? Where will you go to college? Who will you marry? What will your career or calling be? What does the future hold for you? Did you know that when you speak or pray in tongues you are able to "pray out" some of the mysteries concerning your future? As one person put it, "prayer is the track you run on". As you pray and speak in tongues you are praying out mysteries, you are praying out track you will eventually run on. Does that make sense?

2.   1 Corinthians 14:4

What happens to a person who speaks in tongues?_____

Have you ever seen your parents charge the battery to the car? Or have you ever charged rechargeable batteries at home? As long as the batteries are plugged into the battery charger, they will be revived with power and energy! This is the same thing that happens to us when we pray or speak in tongues to God. When we use our secret language, it is like we are plugged into God's battery charger and we get filled with His power and energy.

3.   1 Corinthians 14:18

What did the Apostle Paul say he did more than anyone?_____

4.   1 Corinthians 14:15

What two things did Paul say he could do in the Spirit?

_____

_____

You will find that as you are filled with the Spirit and dilligent to flow in your spiritual language, this experience will make a noted difference in your Christian life. You will find yourself experiencing more power and boldness to be a witness for Christ, more freedom and a greater ease in praying in the Spirit. You'll notice that you are receiving even more revelation from the Word of God and your heart will be satisfied like never before as you speak to God from your heart of hearts in other tongues.

Are you ready to be filled with the Spirit? In the "Real Christians Do It" section, you can walk through the simple steps for receiving the Holy Spirit.

Now it's time to just do it! Let's take action on what we have studied. Would you like to be filled with the Spirit? Would you like more of God's energy to tell others of Jesus? Would you like to have a supernatural code language that you can speak to God?

It's really simple to be filled with the Spirit.

1.   First, you must already be a born-again Christian.

2.   Second, you let God know that you are sorry for any sins you have committed and you let Him know you want every one of His gifts in your life.

3.   Third, you simply ask God the Father to fill you with His Spirit. You can pray a prayer like this:

        Dear Heavenly Father, I ask you in Jesus' Name to fill me with the Holy Spirit. I thank You for Your good gift of the Holy Spirit and I want to be full of Your power and energy so that I can tell everyone about Jesus. I also want to know You better and I want to be able to talk to You from my heart of hearts in the special language of speaking in tongues. Father, I receive Your gift of the Holy Spirit right now. Thank You – in Jesus Name I pray. Amen.

4.   Fourth, now that you have received God's gift, tell Him thank You. Take a moment to praise Him for everything He is doing and is going to do in your life.

5.   Fifth, begin to yield your heart to the Lord in speaking praises and words to Him in other tongues. The Holy Spirit will give you the utterance, as you simply yield your heart and mouth to Him.

I want to encourage you to talk to your parents or your pastor or youth leader about this more. It may be helpful to have them pray with you and coach you more on how you can be filled continually with the Spirit.

How big is your God? Do you believe that with God nothing is impossible? Do you realize that the sky is the limit for you? God is looking for young people who have real faith. He's looking for young people who know Him and who believe His Word! Are you going to be found by God? When His eyes scan the earth, will your faith get His attention? God wants to strengthen those who are fully devoted to Him. If you will stand up and step out as a young person of faith, God will absolutely press His thumbprint all over your life!

Let's look at it this way. God wants you to be a champion for Him! Did you know that anyone in the Bible who was a champion for God was a person with strong faith? People with strong faith see God do awesome things in their lives. God has already given you some faith. You used your faith to believe in Him, didn't you? He has given you a portion of faith. Now it's up to you to add to your faith. It's up to you to grow and develop more faith. God wants you to be a person of great faith!

A.   Pump Up Your Faith Muscles

FAITH MUSCLES: Think of it this way. God has given you muscles, hasn't He? You have biceps, triceps and all kinds of other muscles. I know teens like to tighten their stomachs to see if they can show off a six-pack! They like to pump up their arms to see who has bigger biceps! They like to work out at the gym and bulk up. Your whole body is filled with muscles. You got those muscles when you were born, right? What you do with those muscles is up to you. You can sit on the couch and play video games your whole life and end up being a 50-pound weakling or you can become the strongest kid in the neighborhood by developing your muscles. If you do a few sit ups and push ups, if you play soccer or basketball or do gymnastics, or if you get involved in active sports like snowboarding and skateboarding, you will develop big muscles. These various activities will help you develop bigger, stronger muscles.

If you want really, really big strong muscles, then you will have to be even more dedicated and devoted to exercising and working out than the average kid, right? Think of the weightlifters you see on television. Have you ever seen the power lifters? The ironman? Have you ever seen those muscled bodybuilders up close? The muscles on the men and women who lift weights every day are so big and strong. Those muscles didn't grow by accident; muscular people have to be very disciplined and dedicated to growing their muscles every day.

Did you know it's the same way with our faith? When you became a born-again Christian, God gave you "faith muscles". You have faith for salvation. You have faith for your prayers to be answered. You have faith for lots of things, but at first your faith is small and weak. What you do with your faith muscles is up to you. You can sit in front of the TV and watch DVDs all day, or you can spend all your time listening to CDs and playing on the internet and you'll end up being a weak little baby Christian. People with weak faith muscles are weak spiritually and often these kind of people are directionless, afraid, sad, angry, mean, or not in control of their mouths. Many times, people with weak faith muscles don't know that they can develop their faith muscles to replace their fears with peace, to replace their sadness with joy and laughter, to replace their anger with kindness, to replace their drift-along life with purpose, to replace their mean spirit with God's love and to replace a sassy mouth with words that will bless them and other people.

Do you want to be a teen with weak faith muscles? I hope not! Let's look at how we can have strong faith. How would you like to be a "strong man" spiritually? You can become the strongest spiritual teen in your church or school by developing your faith. How? You'll have to lift spiritual weights each day! Did you know that if you'll take time each day to talk to God, to read your Bible or listen to CDs or DVDs about God's Word, that is just like lifting spiritual weights and it will help you to develop bigger, stronger faith muscles.

Jesus said that we could have faith muscles so strong that we could move mountains! Have you ever faced a mountain or difficulty in your life that you felt you couldn't fix or change? With mountain-moving faith things can change in your life! If you want to have the kind of faith that Jesus tells us to have, if you want mountain-moving faith, then you will have to be more committed and dedicated to praying to God and reading your Bible than the average kid. When you have giant faith muscles nothing is impossible. Jesus said nothing is impossible for those who believe – for those who have muscles of faith!

Are there things or areas in your life where you desire God's supernatural help, provision or favor? Are you an athlete? Are you a computer genius? Are you skilled in art, music or some creative talent? Do you have a dream for your life? Do you envision a big life in God? By being a person who walks and lives by faith, God can touch your life and take you to the next level.

Do you need a car? A job? College funds? Clothes? Do you want more money to give to others? Do you know that God wants to provide for you in all of these areas, but it will require faith? You may have to fight the fight of faith as you believe God and stand strong. But make no mistake, God honors faith and He is the rewarder of those who diligently seek Him! (Hebrews 11:6) Let's look at this.

B.   What Is Faith?

Do you know what faith is? It's really simple. Faith is believing God's Word! When we believe God and His Word, we have faith. When we trust God and His Word, we have faith.

1.   Hebrews 11:1,6

What is faith?_____

Can you please God without faith?_____

What does God do for those who sincerely seek Him?_____

To have faith in God means to have faith in His Word. God wants us to believe everything in His Word. We started our walk of faith when we asked Jesus to come into our hearts. We didn't see Jesus, or feel Jesus, or taste Jesus, or touch Jesus, or smell Jesus – but we knew in our hearts that He was real because we believed God's Word and we invited Him into our lives – right? That is faith!

2.   Hebrews 11:4-30

This is called "God's Hall of Faith"! If you are an outstanding baseball player or football player or basketball player, you might have a chance to someday be in the Hall of Fame, but if you are a person of faith, you can be in God's Hall of Faith! These people used their faith to do mighty things for God. List the name of each person mentioned in the verse:

Verse 4_____

Verse 5_____

Verse 7_____

Verse 8_____

Verse 11_____

Verse 20_____

Verse 21_____

Verse 22_____

Verse 23 _____

Verse 24_____

Verse 29_____

Verse 31_____

Verse 32-33_____

C.   Wimpy Faith Or Strong Faith?

Look up these verses and see if we are learning about wimpy faith or strong faith. Write the word "wimpy" or "strong" next to the verse.

1.   Matthew 6:30_____

2.   Matthew 8:10 (Luke 7:9)_____

3.   Matthew 8:26_____

4.   Matthew 14:31_____

5.   Matthew 15:28_____

6.   Matthew 16:8_____

7.   Romans 4:19_____

88

8.   Romans 4:20_____

D. Growing Stronger In Faith

1.   2 Corinthians 10:15

What does the Apostle Paul hope our faith will do?_____

2.   Romans 10:17

Faith comes when we do what?_____

More faith comes to us when we read and think about God's Word. It's that simple! Faith doesn't come to us by begging for it, desiring it, praying for it, or wishing for it. Faith comes to us one way - faith comes by hearing God's Word. You will have to make a decision to read your Bible - and even better yet, to study your Bible and you will find it will start to fill your heart. You won't have to conjure up faith or strain to have faith; you will simply have faith! Make a decision to saturate yourself, marinate your heart, and wash your mind with God's Word every day and faith will fill your heart!

E. How To Use Your Faith

Our faith muscles need to be used! The way you begin using your faith muscles is by doing something! The way you use the muscles in your body is by doing something! When you exercise, your muscles are used. The way we exercise our faith muscles is by acting on the Word we are believing. The Bible says that faith without actions is dead. (James 2:17) One primary way we get our faith muscles working - to act on the Word - is by putting our mouth to work! When we use our mouth to agree with God's Word, we are acting on the Word. When we say the same thing with our mouths that God's Word says and that we believe in our hearts, we are using our faith. When our heart and our mouth agree, our faith is in action!

Our faith muscle is used when we do this two-part equation.

Believing God's Word in our hearts + Saying God's Word with our mouth = Faith

FAITH IN ACTION: For example, let's say you read Psalm 91 about God's protection. If you believe it, what should you do with your mouth? If we believe in our hearts God's Word in Psalm 91, that God will protect us, and then we say with our mouths, "I am so scared and afraid of everything," what happens? We are believing one thing, but saying something different and our faith won't work! We have a faith muscle, but it is not being used properly and God cannot answer our faith because it is confused. On one hand we say we believe God will protect us, and then with our mouth we say how scared we are. If we really believed God would protect us, what kind of words would we say?

FAITH IN ACTION: Take another example, the story of Daniel. Daniel was a young man who had great faith! He put God first and obeyed God more than anyone else and God blessed him immensely! If you put God first in your life and heart, then you can use your faith to believe God's Word in Daniel 1:17-20 will work for you, too. If you believe this passage in Daniel that shows God will help you with your learning, understanding and schoolwork, but say with your mouth, "I am so stupid and confused," what will happen? God won't be able to answer your faith. Yes, you do have a faith muscle, but it is not being used properly and God cannot answer our faith because it is confused. Can you see that on one hand, we say we believe God will help us with our schoolwork and then with our mouth we say how stupid and confused we are? We are sending a mixed signal to God of faith and unbelief. If we really believed God would help us with our schoolwork, what kind of words would we say?

CRAIG'S STORY: *I want you to read the story of our youth director, Craig. His story is a dramatic tale of how a young kid got hooked on drugs and began running with the wrong crowd. In his teens he found Jesus and began to understand the power of God's Word. The only thing that could break the power of his addiction to drugs was his faith and confession of God's Word.*

I grew up in Southern California near Los Angeles in the 1970's and 80's. My parents brought my brothers and me to church about three times in my life. You could say that I grew up in an agnostic home. We believed that "there was something out there" but we would never really know until we died. When I was in the fourth grade my parents split up and were divorced a year later. I ended up living with my mom who was working as a nurse at the time. It seems like we always had a babysitter around to take care of us. This got me into a lot of trouble. When I was 9 years old, towards the end of my 4th grade I was hanging with my best friend, his older brother, and his older brother's friends. They asked us to smoke some pot with them because they thought it would be funny to see us "high". That was my first experience with drugs. One of these guys was a drug dealer so we got high once a week or so until he got busted a year later.

Also about the same time my best friend and I started sneaking drinks from our parents' liquor cabinets. This ritual of smoking pot and getting drunk continued off and on until I was in 8th grade. Around this time I moved in with my dad and his new family. I was now one of five boys between the ages of 10 and 16, and these new family members helped me add a few extra vices to my repertoire - like stealing, skipping school, shoplifting, sneaking out with my parents' car in the middle of the night, and vandalism. Meanwhile I was maintaining my favorite past time: smoking pot and drinking alcohol.

During my freshman year in high school smoking marijuana or drinking became a daily thing. I also began using crystal methamphetamines and cocaine occasionally. I was extremely interested in music so I went to a lot of concerts where these drugs were an epidemic. I played the guitar in a garage "hair" band called Winged Assasin. We were lame but too high to know it. This band experience led me to meet some real characters who were into Satanism. Having an absence of God in my life and an emptiness in my heart I became hungry. While I was in the 10th grade I started listening to music that was very aggressive and included a lot of Satanic references. I made a decision to become a Satan worshipper, bought a "Satanic Bible", and told my friends and family that I was now a Satanist. I also began holding Satanic rituals with friends. My heart started to get very cold towards people in general and filled with complete hatred towards Christians and God.

Meanwhile my drug habit continued to increase. My addiction was to the point that I only used alcohol when I couldn't find pot, speed, and coke. In the 11th grade I joined a punk band named B.Y.O.D. You can figure out what that meant. The punk crowd opened a whole new world of drugs to me. This is when I began to use LSD, PCP, smoke crack, and using IV drugs. A lot of my friends were "on the run" (homeless), in and out of juvenile hall, drop outs, and outcasts.

By my senior year in high school I was a wreck: hard heart, confused, hurting and hurtful, prideful, daily drug habit, and angry at the One who wanted to save me. I was barely going to school and barely passing my classes. My parents didn't know how to help me, but God did. He started to reach out to me through many avenues that year. There was a bass player named Randy in my band. Randy was a born again/backslidden Christian. He would always tell me about God and I would preach my "Satanism" to him. We constantly went back and forth with our argument. Just as our band was starting to get a lot of gigs and gain local popularity, Randy quit the band because he had "recommitted" his life back to Christ.

I was confused by this. The band fell apart shortly after that. Randy would come around about once a month to invite me to a Bible study, but I refused to go.

About the same time this group of Christians would come to the park where all the "punkers" hung out and partied. They wanted to share Christ with us. They were relentless and didn't seem to mind that my friends and I would cuss them out. They kept coming back (thank God).

About January 1987 I began watching a preacher on TV. I was still a Satanist but this guy intrigued me. He wasn't like the average TV preacher that I was so critical of. In March that year I agreed to go to Randy's home Bible study. My heart was so cold and down for so long that being at this Bible study was the first time I could remember feeling happy since I was a little kid. When he dropped me off at I home afterward I was back to my same miserable self.

During that same month, I was watching a TV preacher one day and this guy told people if they were ready to receive Christ that they should call the number on the screen. Right there, in front of my two non-Christian brothers, I decided I was ready. When I picked up the phone my brothers started laughing at me and said, "What are you doing?" I looked at them and began to cry while I said, "I am accepting Christ." So, in front of my brothers, I dialed the number and prayed over the phone with a counselor. I was now a Christian!

The next day I woke up and got ready for school. I still had a drug habit. I went to steal money from my step-mom's purse. For the first time I could remember I actually felt guilty about stealing. My heart was changed and I put the money back. The strange thing was that I continued to do a lot of the ungodly things I did before I prayed to be saved, but now I felt guilty about them. Before I was a Christian I had been oblivious concerning right from wrong, so for two months after I prayed to accept Christ I lived an even more miserable life because I was conscious of the ungodly way I was living.

In May 1987 Randy and the guitar player from the band invited me to church on a Sunday night. This was a small church. I walked in looking like a punk with a shirt that read in bold letters "RUN-DMC RAISING HELL". Needless to say I was sticking out like a sore thumb. At the end of the message they approached me and asked if I wanted to be saved. I told them I already was. They didn't believe me! I agreed to pray with them at the altar and it was at this time that I fully 100% committed my life to Christ.

After that, I began to read the Bible, pray and attend church. I quit hanging out with my drug addict friends and found some Christian friends. I told a lot of people in my school about Jesus and how He changed my life. They laughed, but I didn't care. My family thought I was nuts, but I didn't care. God had set me on the right path for my life. Old friends I would run into could see a physical difference in my countenance. My life had changed dramatically, but there was still one thing I needed to overcome, and I found out that God had given me enough faith to win!

I didn't use any drugs or alcohol for the first three weeks after my recommitment to Christ, but by week four the temptations came! It didn't help that I was working a part time job at a convenience store that sold a lot of alcohol and I worked with people that were into partying. The first time a coworker asked me to smoke a joint with him I physically shook because it was so tempting. I yielded to the temptation and smoked the joint. What a miserable feeling. I felt like I wasn't even a Christian anymore. During the next two months I yielded to the temptation of using crystal methamphetamines, marijuana and alcohol. It was not that I wanted to do drugs: I didn't know how to resist the temptation. The devil was saying to me "you will always be a drug addict, this Christianity thing isn't real, you will never change". I was starting to feel that way.

My Christian friends helped me know that I was still saved and showed me how to pray for forgiveness. This is also when I learned how to stand in faith and believe God's Word! Even though I was still using drugs, I didn't stop going to church or reading Christian books and the Bible. I learned about the importance of confessing the Word of God. I learned I needed to confess the Word as true regardless of my present circumstances. I found a scripture in Colossians 1:13 that says, "Who hath delivered us from the power of darkness, and hath translated us into the kingdom of his dear Son" I was excited to see that it said I was already delivered from the power of darkness.

For several weeks I began to confess this scripture out loud for about 30 minutes a day. I would include my name. I would say, " I, Craig, am delivered from the power of darkness. Darkness includes drugs and alcohol. I am already free from drugs and alcohol because God delivered me. I'm not going to be, I already am free." Did I feel free? No. The temptation was just as strong as before. In fact, I used drugs on the same days that I read this scripture. I kept at it though. In my heart I knew the Word of God was more real than my body's craving for drugs. After two weeks of confessing Collosians 1:13, I was stronger spiritually, but I was still working the same job and during a one week period I had three big temptations. A guy came into the store and asked us to smoke his favorite type of pot with him: "Christmas Tree Sess". This was also my favorite pot that was only available once a year. I wanted to smoke it soooo badly. Immediately I began quoting Colossians 1:13 under my breath. After a few minutes I declined. That was victory number one.

93

A day later I was sweeping the parking lot and found a dime bag of crystal meth. A lot of drugs were used and dealt at this store, so this was not too uncommon. This was another one of those temptations that made me shake. Colossians 1:13 came out of my mouth again. I swept up the bag and put it in the trash! The third victory came a few days later when again I was sweeping the parking lot and found another bag of crystal meth. I was stronger now but still quoted Colossians 1:13. That was the last real temptation that I had with drugs or alcohol. That was 16 years ago! I learned first hand the power of faith in God's Word!

Can you see how important it is to say words that agree with God's Words; to say words that you believe in your heart?

1.   2 Corinthians 4:13

        I believed and therefore I _____

2.   Romans 10:8-10

        If you_____ that Jesus is Lord

        If you_____ that God raised Him from the dead

        You will_____

3.   Mark 11:22-23

        God wants us to develop mountain-moving faith! Mountains can represent any difficulty in your life. Is there an obstacle in your life? Is something really bothering you and trying to get you down? You need to use your mountain-moving faith!

        In verse 22, what did Jesus tell us to have?_____

        In verse 23, do we pray to the mountain?_____

        In verse 23, do we pray to God about the mountain?_____

        In verse 23, do we speak to the mountain?_____

        What will obey our command?_____

When we speak words of faith, what are we to have in our hearts?_____

Develop your own personal plan for growing in faith by taking a look at the "Real Christians Do It" segment.

Now it's time to just do it! Let's take action on what we've studied. Do you want to be one of God's super strong faith muscle teens? How are you going to develop your faith muscles? It will take more commitment than some other young people are willing to give. You don't want to be a wimpy Christian, do you? Are you willing to discipline yourself to read God's Word every day? Are you willing to give up some of your time playing video games or computer games to read God's Word? Are you willing to give up some of your free time to put God's Word first? Are you willing to get your mouth in agreement with God's Word, even when you don't feel like it? Are you willing to give up some of the negative words you are in the habit of saying? If you will, God will truly bless your life!

Your heart will get so full of God's Word that as you speak God's Word out, you will release a powerful force called faith. Mountains will move in your life and your name can be written in God's Hall of Faith.

In case you didn't develop a personal plan for reading your Bible as we discussed in Chapter 3, here's another chance to discipline yourself and make time for reading your Bible. What type of commitment are you willing to make?

YOUR PERSONAL PLAN: What is your plan for developing your faith muscles?

I want to read my Bible for _____ minutes each day.

I want to read my Bible during this time each day:_____

I would suggest that you talk to your parents about getting the New Testament on audiotape or CD and play it each night before you go to bed. Let God's Word begin to fill your heart and watch those faith muscles grow!

MY FAITH ADVENTURE:

I am believing God for:_____

I base my faith on the following verses:_____

A.   Blessed Or Loserville?

God wants your life blessed. Did you know that? He really does. There is a life that God blesses. There is a life that God offers where you don't have to be depressed, sad, mad, unhappy, rebellious, suicidal, disappointed, guilt-ridden, fearful, overwhelmed and stressed out. You can have real joy and happiness, peace, freedom from fear, good friends, and a healthy, good life with good stuff.

There is also a life that God cannot bless. Did you know God will allow you to choose to have a bad attitude, to disobey Him and your parents, to have a rebellious heart, or an apathetic heart toward Him? Did you know He'll let you party, smoke, sleep around, lie, steal and live a life that doesn't honor or please the Lord? He will. He'll also let you experience the results of that life. He'll let you reap what you sow. Unfortunately, many times the results are young people who die early, or experience weakness and sickness; young people who are unhappy and depressed; young people that find themselves lonely in a crowd or big party. They find out that while they are surrounded by "so-called" friends, in reality their "friends" are just as selfish as they are. Young people that don't choose to please the Lord may ultimately end up as poor, broke losers used by the devil to live evil, boring, empty lives. Not a pretty picture is it? We get to choose the type of life we want to have - a blessed life or a life God cannot bless.

We see examples in the Bible of people who lived a life that pleased the Lord - they listened to His Word and they obeyed it, and they were blessed by the Lord. If you study the Old Testament you will find that everytime God's people faced trouble – early death, sickness, the wilderness, being overcome by enemies, tragedy and destruction – it was the direct result of their rebellion and disobedience. It wasn't God desire for them, but whenever they chose to disobey and walk away from God they experienced a defeated life. However, whenever they returned to the Lord with their whole heart, listened to His Word, remembered His promises and obeyed Him, they enjoyed forgiveness and lived long lives full of strength, health, good friends, wealth, influence, and they were mightily used by God.

What kind of life do you want? Let's see what the Bible says about the life God has for you.

B.   The Life God Wants You To Have

1.   John 10:10

What does Jesus want us to have?_____

What does the thief (the devil) want us to have?_____

2.   Psalm 103:1-5

What does God want us to never forget?_____

What does God do to all of our sins?_____

What does God do to all of our diseases?_____

3.   3 John 2

What did the Apostle John pray for his friends?_____

4.   Deuteronomy 28:1-14

In verses 1-2, what will God do in our lives if we fully obey Him?_____

In verses 3-14, list all the blessings God has promised us:

_____

_____

_____

Read verses 15-68, to discover the life God doesn't want for you!

5.   Deuteronomy 30:15,19-20

God is giving us a choice. What are our choices?

_____   _____

What does God want us to choose?_____

If we choose to love the Lord our God and to obey His Word, what does He promise?

_____

We've told our teenagers that God has a "blessed life" for them! If they will make pleasing the Lord their priority, His blessings will overtake them! Our daughter Annie is in middle school and she is learning how to make choices that please the Lord.

ANNIE'S STORY: *I have grown up in a Christian home and my parents are pastors. I became a Christian when I was very young. Even though I have been a Christian all of my life, I still have many questions about lots of things that have to do with the Bible, being a Christian and dealing with school, and the temptations that everyone goes through no matter if they're a Christian, a pastor's kid, or a normal person.*

Most of the time, being a Christian has really helped me with my decisions and it has made school and life a lot easier, but there have also been times when I made bad choices and I have learned that God will forgive you and help you.

At school there is one kid who knows that I am a Christian and a pastor's kid and sometimes he tries to be a smart aleck by making fun of me. For instance, he acts like he is making decisions for me with comments like, "...she wants to do this because she is a Christian..." He thinks he's funny and I have to tell myself that even though it kind of hurts and bugs me that he makes fun of my being a Christian, when it comes to me and the Lord, I would rather please the Lord than please a few people by denying my Christian faith.

When I face hard times the Lord helps me by reassuring me with what I have read in the Bible and He reminds me that in the end, pleasing Him is better. So, being a Christian makes life so much easier and I really love that I have a Christian home to grow up in.

Did you know that God wants you to be blessed, but He won't force His blessings on you? He lets you choose! When you love the Lord and obey His Word you are choosing His blessings. He wants others to see His blessing in your life. He wants you to be blessed so that you can bless others. You are a kid of the King! Kings' kids are different from those in the world, aren't they? They are very blessed and they are expected to live a life that fits being a king's kid! Is that what you choose?

C.   God Wants You To Be Happy & Healthy

1.   Exodus 15:26

God does not want us to suffer with disease. He wants us to be healthy and healed.

What did God call Himself?_____

2.   Psalm 103:1-3

What is God's promise concerning our diseases?_____

3.   1 Peter 2:24

When Jesus died on the cross He took our sins, and by His wounds we are_____

4.   Proverbs 4:20-22

What are we supposed to pay close attention to?_____

How are we to listen?_____

If we let God's Word penetrate deep into our hearts, what will it bring to us?

_____

5.   James 5:16

If you are sick, what can you do?_____

What can you be sure of, if the elders of the church anoint you with oil and pray the prayer of faith?

_____

If you have sinned, what will God do for you?_____

6.   Matthew 8:8-10, 9:22, 29, 15:28, Mark 2:5, 5:24, 10:52, Luke 7:9, 8:48, 17:19, 18:42

What do these verses say you can receive by your faith?

_____

7.   Proverbs 12:18

Your words play a huge role! You can bring healing to yourself or to others.

What kind of words don't bring healing?_____

What do the words of the wise bring?_____

8.   Proverbs 15:4

What kind of words bring life and health?_____

Can you think of an example of this kind of words?_____

What kind of words wouldn't be gentle?_____

9.   Proverbs 16:24

What type of words bring health to the body and sweetness to your soul (your mind and emotions)?

_____

10. Proverbs 18:21

The words of your tongue can bring_____ or_____

D. God Wants You To Have A Rich And Generous Life

Some Christians think that God wants them to live on barely get along street all their lives. No, God wants your life to be blessed even with finances and material things - however, often times before you can have these things, He has to be certain <u>they</u> won't have you! God wants to be the Supreme love of your heart and He doesn't want you to put money, cars, computers, stereos and stuff ahead of Him. When Jesus finds teenagers that are on-fire for Him and sold out to Him, He delights in blessing them with His wisdom and prosperity! Jesus said in Matthew 6:21, "Wherever your treasure is, there your heart and thoughts will also be." (NLT) So, it's important to keep Jesus as the treasure of your heart and thoughts! Let's look at a few verses that talk about money and things and heart motivations, and then let's look at God's desire to bless our lives.

1. Philippians 4:11-13

What did Paul say he had learned? (verse. 11.)_____

2. 1 Timothy 66

Godliness + _____ = Great Gain

3. Hebrews 13:5

What does God tell us concerning contentment?_____

Did you know that sometimes before God can bless you with a new pair of jeans, you need to be content with the jeans you have? Before God can bless you with a new car, you need to be content with (and thankful for) the car you have! Prove to God that He, not "stuff", has your heart by being a person who is thankful for the stuff you have! Better yet, show God that He is more important than your stuff by prayerfully asking Him if you should give any of it to other teens who are not so blessed? It's good to occassionally check up on your heart and ask yourself how you would feel if God asked you to give away some of your favorite things. Could you do it? Would you do it? When your heart is in the right place, then you just watch and see how God will bless your life! Let's look at several verses that tell us about God's will to prosper and bless us.

4.   Deuteronomy 8:18

Who gives the power to become rich?_____

What are we to remember?_____

5.   Philippians 4:19

What will God supply?_____

6.   Malachi 3:10

What does God want us to give to Him?_____

What will God do for us?_____

7.   Luke 6:38

What are we to do?_____

What will happen if we become giving people?_____

What type of things can we give to people? _____

Have you thought of giving compliments, smiles, friendly notes, any of your stuff or other things that are valuable to you? Did you know that lots of young people are selfish? They are thinking "me" and "mine". They are not thinking about "you" and "yours". They are not thinkng of sharing! But, if you will learn to share the things you have with others and be a generous giver when you are a young person, the Lord will bless your life. He will be sure you have more than enough stuff!

8.   Proverbs 11:25

Who prospers?_____

9.   2 Corinthians 9:6-8

We can give a little or we can give a lot! God compares our giving to a farmer planting seeds. If a farmer plants a few corn seeds, how big will his corn crop be? If a farmer plants a lot of corn seeds, how big will his corn harvest be?

When we give, what should our attitude be?_____

Should we feel pressured to give?_____

What does God love?_____

E.   The Secret To Living Life To The Max

1.   Deuteronomy 29:9

Remember these two words: Listen & Obey! If we will listen to God and His Word and then obey the things He tells us, we will live an abundant life to the max! Remember you have to choose!

You will prosper in everything you do if you do what?_____

2.   Isaiah 1:19

If we will obey God and let Him help us, what are we promised?_____

Does having "plenty to eat" sound like prosperity?_____

Let's look at this more in the "Real Christians Do It" segment.

Let's take action on what we've studied. I want you to take a few moments to think about your relationship with the Lord.

Is there any area of your life in which God has asked you to do something? To not do something? For example, has He told you to obey your parents? Has He told you to forgive others? Has He told you to love people? Has He told you to honor your teacher? Has He told you to quit saying certain bad words? Has He told you to quit getting high? Has He told you to be generous toward others? Has He asked you to give something to someone else to bless them? Has He asked you to apologize?

In your conscience, is there any area of your life that God wants you to correct because right now that area is not pleasing to Him?

Are you willing to obey the Lord in these areas? Are you ready to choose life?

Why not make a list of the actions you are going to take immediately, in obedience to God.

_____

_____

God wants you to live the life He blesses and it begins with your making good choices. Do it!

<table>
<tr><td>CHAPTER 11</td><td>Being A Winner
"How To Be Be An Overcomer"</td></tr>
</table>

Ever felt like a major geek? Mayor of Loserville? Ever been mad at yourself? Have you ever felt defeated? Did you ever feel like a failure in school? Have you felt ugly? Have you felt lonely? Did you ever do something totally embarrassing? Have you ever felt sad or mad toward your friends? Parents? Brothers or sisters? Ever felt like you were not included in the group? Felt rejected? Have you ever struggled with your thought life?

We've all faced hard times. Facing hard times is a normal part of life, but as Christians God wants us to know how to trust God so that we get up, shake ourselves off and follow the Lord as He leads us to victory. As we walk through life, there will sometimes be roadblocks. Sometimes we will face challenges or difficulties that the Lord wants to help us win. These roadblocks and challenges sometimes come because we made a dumb choice, sometimes the devil tries to put difficulties in our path, and sometimes just because we live in a fallen world we will face trouble. The good news is that no matter what you face, God can show you how to win. Jesus has made a way for us to have the victory in every area of our lives. Sometimes you will have to be patient and fight the fight of faith while God is leading you to victory, but in the end you will win because God has made you a winner!

Have you ever played tennis, chess, snowboarding, skiing, skateboarding or some other type of individual sport? Before the game, did you begin to picture or visualize your strategy and how you were going to be the winner? Have you pictured yourself hitting perfect tennis shots in a really hard tennis game? Have you pictured yourself snowboarding or skiing down a hill and carving every giant, Olympic-sized mogul just perfectly? Have you imagined yourself doing motocross or skateboarding tricks at the X Games and landing every ride just perfectly? In order to win, you have to begin to see yourself as a winner. We are going to face pressures, opponents and Olympic-sized problems, but God wants us to imagine ourselves winning through every difficulty.

A.   God Sees Us As Winners

How does God see us as winners? We need to see ourselves the way God sees us!

1.   Romans 8:31, 37

Who is always for us, on our side?_____

If God is for us, who can be against us?_____

2. 1 Corinthians 15:57

Who do we give thanks to?_____

What does He always give us?_____

We have victory through who?_____

3. 2 Corinthians 2:14

Who do we give thanks to?_____

How often do we triumph or have the victory?_____

4. 1 John 5:4-5

Are you a child of God?_____

What will God always give you?_____

Who wins the battle?_____

5. Psalm 34:19

Who faces troubles?_____

What does the Lord do for us?_____

6. Philippians 4:13

How many things can I do through Christ?_____

What does God give me?_____

Don't try to do things in your own strength. You can't give yourself the victory – only God can do that as you trust Him. Always remember that God is on your side - you have Jesus giving you victory and the Holy Spirit who helps you in all you do. You are on a winning team and God calls you a winner! God's team always wins!

B.   The Winning Team

The Bible tells us that there are two kingdoms, or we could say two teams: the kingdom of light, or God's kingdom, and the kingdom of darkness, or Satan's kingdom. These two kingdoms, or teams, are against each other. Jesus died on a cross so that all of us who were in Satan's kingdom of darkness could be switched to God's team - the kingdom of light. Jesus went to the cross so we could be drafted and picked up to be on God's team!

1.   Colossians 1:13

What "team" did God rescue us from?_____

What "team" has God brought us into?_____

2.   John 10:10

Jesus told us what His purpose is. What does Jesus want to bring you?_____

Satan's goal is different. What three things does Satan do?

_____   _____   _____

C.   We Have God's Power

God sees us as winners in Christ. God has placed us on His winning team. He wants us to act like winners and He wants us to stop our enemy from having any influence in our lives. Satan wanted to be God. He lost! The devil wants to be god in different areas of our lives, and it's our job to kick him out! We need to ignore the devil's suggestions and tell him that we are going to obey God! Let's look at the power God has given to us in Jesus.

1.   Satan Does Not Want Us To Know About Our Power

    a.   1 Peter 5:8,9

            What does the devil want to do?_____

            What are we supposed to do?_____

    b.   2 Corinthians 2:11

            God does not want Satan to outsmart us.

            What are we to be familiar with?_____

            If you want to know what the devil's evil schemes are, you can look up these
            verses. We can see what type of tricks the devil is up to when we read these
            verses. How do these verses describe the devil?

            John 8:44_____   John 10:10_____

            Revelation 12:10_____   1 Peter 5:8_____

            2 Corinthians 11:14_____   Acts 10:38_____

            Mark 4:15_____   Luke 22:31_____

2.   Jesus Wants Us To Know About Our Power

    a.   Luke 10:19

            What did Jesus give us?_____

            Whose power is greater – Jesus' power or the devil's power?_____

            What can hurt you?_____

b. 1 John 4:4

Who is in us?_____

Who is greater?_____

Remember you have God living inside of you! You and God are a majority! You are never alone, but the Almighty God lives inside of you and He is greater than any enemy you'll ever face!

c. Revelation 17:14

Who is Lord of lords?_____

Who is King of kings?_____

Who wins?_____

What does God say about us - His chosen ones?_____

Jesus is the King and we are the kings. Jesus is the Lord and we are the lords. Jesus defeats the devil! He gives us His victory. Jesus gave us weapons to use to enforce Satan's defeat. Let's see what weapons God has given us.

D. God Has Given Us Weapons

1. Hebrews 4:12 – God's Word Is A Weapon

What kind of weapon is God's word compared to?_____

When we know, believe and quote God's Word, it's just like sticking a dagger into the devil. He hates God's Word and it's one of our strong weapons!

2. Luke 10:17, Philippians 2:9,10 – Jesus' Name Is A Weapon

Who has to bow down when we use Jesus' Name?_____

Every name has to bow down to Jesus' Name. The devil and his demons are paralyzed when we use Jesus' Name.

3.   Philippians 4:8 – Using Our Mind To Think About God's Word Is A Weapon

What are we to make our minds think about?_____

It is really important for us to be very careful about what we think. If we have a bad or evil thought, we immediately need to replace that thought with a thought from God. If we think of the things the devil wants us to think about – like scary things, evil things, bad things, fearful things, disobedient things, curse words, harmful things, illegal things, stealing, killing, and perverse things - our minds will be filled with fear and confusion. These kinds of thoughts can even give us bad dreams. If we think of the things God wants us to think about – like loving people, being nice, being generous, obeying our parents, being respectful to teachers and adults, happy things, fun things, pure things – our minds will be filled with peace and joy. These kinds of thoughts give us a happy life!

WHAT TO DO WITH YOUR THOUGHTS: What do you do if you have a bad thought? You replace it! Here's an example. What if I tell you to think about a pink elephant? What are you now thinking of? A pink elephant, right? What if I told you to stop thinking about the pink elephant, could you? It would be hard to just stop thinking of the pink elephant. Instead of trying to stop thinking of a thought, you need to replace the thought with something else. So, what if I said to replace your thought of the pink elephant with a thought of a blue frog. Now what are you thinking about? You are thinking about a blue frog, right? By replacing our bad thoughts with good thoughts from God's Word, we can control our thoughts to be in line with God's desire. This is a great weapon to use when the devil tries to give you his thoughts – just replace the devil's thoughts with God's thoughts!

What do these verses say about our thoughts?

Isaiah 26:3_____

Romans 12:1-2_____

2 Corinthians 10:4-5_____

Let's take action on what we've studied. God has made you winner! He has put you on His winning team! God has given you power and weapons so that you can always win! Thank God for Jesus, His shed blood on the cross, the Word of God and the Name of Jesus! Be sure to focus your thoughts on God's Word, and you will live the life of victory on God's winning team. No matter how hard your opponent fights against you, you are a winner!

Are you stuggling with your thoughts? Here's a great exercise that will help you.

Let's read Ephesians 6:10-18

"A final word: Be strong with the Lord's mighty power. Put on all of God's armor so that you will be able to stand firm against all strategies and tricks of the Devil. For we are not fighting against people made of flesh and blood, but against the evil rulers and authorities of the unseen world, against those mighty powers of darkness who rule this world, and against wicked spirits in the heavenly realms. Use every piece of God's armor to resist the enemy in the time of evil, so that after the battle you will still be standing firm. Stand your ground, putting on the sturdy belt of truth and the body armor of God's righteousness. For shoes, put on the peace that comes from the Good News, so that you will be fully prepared. In every battle you will need faith as your shield to stop the fiery arrows aimed at you by Satan. Put on salvation as your helmet, and take the sword of the Spirit, which is the word of God." (NLT)

Notice that we are told to put on the armor of God. List the pieces of the armor below:

_____   _____

_____   _____

_____   _____

The devil likes to throw thoughts like "fiery arrows" at our mind. These fiery arrows will always contradict God's Word. They will be lies. They will be full of defeat, accusation, fear and deceit. Can you think of any fiery arrows the devil has tried to throw at you?

Here's what you should do: Take up your shield of faith! Get an index card and write out a Scripture that tells you the truth from God's Word. This is your shield of faith and any time the devil throws a fiery dart at you, just hold up your shield and begin to say what the Bible says!

od has a job for you to do! Did you know that? Have you ever asked questions like: Why am I here? What is my purpose? God does have a special plan for you. You are here for a purpose! He knows you better than anyone and He wants the very best for your life. It's important to know the path God wants you to follow so that you can walk right into His best plan for you. You can't get this plan from anyone else and you can't copy others; you just need to follow God from your heart. Get this in your heart right now: "God has a special plan for me and He wants to use me in a mighty way!" Let's look at this.

A.   You Are God's Minister

Did you know that you are already a minister? Maybe you aren't called "Pastor" or "Reverend", but you are a minister for God!

1.   2 Corinthians 5:18

What task has God given you?_____

What do you think "reconciliation" means?_____

RECONCILIATION: This is a big word which means "restoration to divine favor." In modern language, we would say God wants people to know that He is not mad at them and He wants to be friends with them.

God has a job for you to do! Let's look at some of the jobs God asks His children to do.

2.   1 Corinthians 12:28

Did you know God has placed us in His family right where He wants us? In verse 28, He describes some of the jobs God wants different people to do. Do you see the list? Besides "healing", what other ministry starts with an "H"?

"those who can _____ others."

The first job you get to do for God is to simply help others! It's called the ministry of helps! Look at the people in your family, your friends, schoolmates and the people at church and see if there are ways you can help others. This is your first ministry – helping others!

3.   Matthew 20:26-28

If you want to be great in God's kingdom and if you want to be a leader, what must you do?

_____

Even Jesus didn't come to be served, but to do what?_____

How could you serve your family and friends better?_____

4.   Matthew 7:12

How should you treat others?_____

5.   John 6:5-13

Let's look at a young boy that God used as His minister. This boy gave Jesus what he had and Jesus performed a miracle!

What did the little boy give?

Five barley _____   Two small _____

In verse 10, how many men were present and fed?_____

Before Jesus passed out the food, what did He do?_____

How many baskets were filled after everyone ate?_____

B.   You Are God's Messenger

1.   Mark 16:15

What did Jesus tell us to do?_____

2.   Matthew 5:14-16

What did Jesus call you?_____

What are we supposed to do with our light?_____

When we do good deeds, our light is shining and people see our Heavenly Father in our lives!

Can you think of a good deed that you've done recently?_____

3.   Matthew 4:19

Who does Jesus want you to follow?_____

What will Jesus make you to become?_____

4.   Luke 15:3-7

How does God feel about lost people?_____

What does He do when a lost person, a sinner, turns to God?_____

5.   1 Corinthians 9:19-23

What does this passage tell us about being relatable to others, so that we can win them to Christ?

_____

_____

117

Have you ever witnessed to others about the Lord? Have you tried to find common ground with other people so that you could win them to Christ? Or, have you been embarrassed? Too shy? Fearful? Have you ever really thought about the fact that people that don't know Jesus are really missing out? They are missing out on the joy of knowing Him and they are missing out on the opportunity to go to heaven. Hell is a real place, you know. We don't want anyone to spend eternity there. So, who do you know that is not saved? Who do you know that needs to know Jesus? Why not pray and see if the Lord will help you to share the gospel with them. Be bold and begin to talk about Jesus to your friends and family.

C.   God Has A Plan For Your Life

1.   Jeremiah 29:11

What kind of plan does God have for your life?_____

2.   Ephesians 2:10

What does God call you?_____

What has God planned for us to do?_____

3.   1 Peter 4:10

What has God given to you?_____

If we discover these gifts and use them, what can flow through us?_____

As you get older, you will begin to notice certain talents and gifts that God has given you. Are you a good speaker or actor who loves to talk in front of people? Are you gifted to draw or write or create things? Maybe you are gifted in sports or in building things. Maybe you are an organizer or a real people friendly type person. Each person has special gifts and talents from God. We are all unique and special, and once we understand our gifts and talents, we will be able to use them to serve God in a special way.

Let's take action on what we've studied. It's time to pray and think about serving God by doing something nice and by telling someone about Jesus.

Let's see...

SERVE GOD BY DOING SOMETHING NICE

If you were going to do something nice and helpful for one person, so that they could know God's love, which person would you pick?

_____

What nice thing do you want to do for this person?_____

When will you do it?_____

SERVE GOD BY TELLING SOMEONE ABOUT JESUS

Who do you know that doesn't know Jesus?_____

If you were going to witness to one of your friends about Jesus, what would you say?

_____

Why not obtain a gospel tract like The Four Spiritual Laws and practice sharing it with one of your Christian friends first, then pray and share it with a person who doesn't know Jesus?

When will you share Jesus with this person?_____

About The Author

Beth Jones is a Bible teacher, columnist, wife and mother of four children who ministers the Word in a relevant and inspiring way by sharing down-to-earth insights. She is the author of the *Bite Sized Bible Study Series*, the popular *Getting A Grip On The Basics Series*, and the new *Get A Grip Minibook Series* - aka: *Get A Grip Mini's*. She and her husband, Jeff, serve as the senior pastors of Kalamazoo Valley Family Church. To find out more about the author or to read real stories from others who use these resources, visit **bethjones.org** or **kvfc.org**.

Beth may be contacted @ www.bethjones.org

Kalamazoo Valley Family Church

995 Romence Road

Portage, MI 49024

269-324-5599

www.kvfc.org

BethJones**.org**

a simple casual website

articles and bible studies

topics like eternal life, girl stuff, healing, ministry,

finances, holy spirit, prayer, victory, faq

click it